Francis
Camps

Robert Jackson

Francis
Camps

Famous Case Histories of
the Celebrated Pathologist

Hart-Davis, MacGibbon
London

Granada Publishing Limited
First published in Great Britain 1975 by Hart-Davis MacGibbon Ltd
Frogmore, St Albans, Hertfordshire AL2 2NF and
3 Upper James Street, London W1R 4BP

ISBN 0 246 10738 3
Printed in Great Britain by
Northumberland Press Limited, Gateshead

Contents

List of Illustrations between pages 96 and 97

Author's Note

I have been helped by many people in writing this book but I wish
particularly to express my indebtedness to the following who have given
me freely of their time and the benefit of their expert knowledge:
Dr J. W. Brooke-Barnett; Dr M. G. Gill-Carey; Dr R. A. K. Clarke;
Dr E. T. Cleghorn; Dr Barbara Dodd; Professor Richard J. Harrison;
Dr J. D. Harte; Dr H. R. M. Johnson; Lord Justice Lawton; Miss Rachel
Langridge; Mr D. M. Leach; Dr I. M. Librach; Mr David Napley;
Mr Frederick Oughton; Dr Ann Peach; Dr P. R. Stevens; Professor R.
Donald Teare; Dr Gavin Thurston; the editors of *The Lancet*,
British Medical Journal, *Kent Messenger* and *Chelmsford Weekly
News*.

On information available, I have estimated that Professor Camps
performed at least eighty-eight thousand post mortems in the course of
his life as a professional pathologist. Obviously the details of no more
than a fraction of that staggering total can find a place in this book. In the
course of selection, I have tried to include those with an interesting
medical or legal background and those that qualify by virtue of human
interest.

R. J.

One

Francis Edward Camps

Francis Edward Camps, Professor of Forensic Medicine at the famous London Hospital Medical College in Whitechapel, was a most unusual man, with a most unusual and, some would say, macabre job. He had many of the same qualities that made his great friend, Sir Bentley Purchase, the eccentric he was: one an outstanding pathologist, the other the leading coroner of his day.

They came from the same kind of social background. Purchase was the son of a wealthy straw hat manufacturer and Camps, born in 1905, was one of the three sons of an even wealthier general practitioner and surgeon, Dr P. W. L. Camps, who made a great deal of money ministering to the rich burgesses of the then fashionable suburb of Teddington. Old Dr Camps qualified in 1895 and, although he was charming and efficient, he was inclined to be difficult. He had a habit of calling in specialists but always making it plain that he, and not the specialist, was in sole charge of the case.

Camps' mother, his 'Ma' in later life, was a somewhat forbidding *grande dame*, who had her views and always let everybody know what they were. When Camps grew older and the family lived in Cambridge, he was always up before his mother for inspection before he went to a party. If his appearance did not come up to standard, he was required to return to his room to make good the deficiencies. It was a happy, typically well-to-do Edwardian household. Camps always spoke affectionately of his parents, and when he went to Marlborough College it was a rather more spartan extension of his home. He was happy there, too.

Francis Camps was the only one of his brothers to take up medicine. When he left Marlborough College, he enrolled at Guy's Hospital Medical School and qualified at twenty-three. At this stage of his life, he had no thought of specializing; it probably never entered his head that one day he would be a front-rank pathologist. In fact he had no idea what he wanted to do. There were jobs for doctors available in the rather unpleasantly hot places administered by the Colonial Service and, being a young man, Camps was eager to see something of the world before he settled down to steady practice as a G.P. Part of the attraction of a Colonial Service appointment was that when he had finished his service abroad he could apply for a course, with full pay, on the further study of tropical diseases.

The war came when Camps' plan was about to mature and instead of heading for the tropics he found himself travelling no further afield than Chelmsford, where he became a junior doctor at a flourishing local clinic, founded by Sir Arthur Hurst. He remained for a time as a resident medical officer. He then left to join another local practice, one of the partners of which was a physician at the Chelmsford and Essex Hospital. Camps was soon doing duties there, as well as taking his part in the practice. His work was onerous but young doctors were accustomed to hard work and Camps had ample energy to cope with it. He was naturally an early riser and after several telephone alarm calls between five-thirty and six he would rise and take a leisurely bath while he thought about the problems he knew were facing him. He would probably have had no more than four or five hours' sleep.

The problems were daunting enough. After attending morning surgery, he would visit his seriously ill or bed-ridden patients and at eleven o'clock he was doing his rounds of the wards at the hospital. In the afternoon and evening, he was back at the hospital attending to out-patients, his evening surgery or private patients. After supper, when most other men would be thinking of bed, he would go to the mortuary to begin his pathology, which would go on until he had finished all there was to do. It was not unusual for the session to last until four o'clock in the morning and his medical assistants and technicians were required to be present for as long as he was there. To Camps a yawn from a student or houseman or a momentary closing of the eyes in the small hours indicated boredom, which Camps was not slow to rebuke. He could not understand tiredness or the desire to sleep any more than he would understand illness. Dr Hugh R. M. Johnson, his principal assistant for many years later on at the London Hospital, recalls how an early morning session at the mortuary was usually followed by an invitation to Camps' flat in Welbeck Street for a drink and a talk over the day's events. Camps was so exhausted that he would often fall asleep in the middle of a sentence. An hour of ordinary conversation with Camps was an exhausting experience, according to Dr Johnson, but when the talk was laced with technicalities it was very difficult indeed for initiates to follow. Even Johnson, a much younger man and a practised long-distance listener, sometimes succumbed to the temptation to close his eyes. Camps immediately would be full of concern. 'Are you tired, my boy?' he would say anxiously. 'You must really go to bed and get some sleep.' It would be perhaps four o'clock in the morning.

An American student, to whom Camps generously lent a room in his flat whilst he was doing some research in the forensic department at the London Hospital, used to complain good-humouredly that he could not sleep because of Camps' habitual rustling of his papers up to two, three and four in the morning.

Conversation was difficult with Camps, not only because he liked to monopolize it but because he 'butterflied' from one subject to another. He expected listeners to follow his unspoken thoughts. If he said 'You remember the case of the black man from Deptford?' what he really meant was the case of the Chinese woman from Lewisham, and he expected his colleagues and students to realize this. He did not appreciate the difficulties that arose from this habit.

Camps' first speciality when he decided to break out of general practice was obstetrics, but in 1935 he realized that it did not interest him enough to make it his life's work. He opted for pathology. Camps, who was then thirty, was in the field with a handicap, compared with the other two leading pathologists, Professors Keith Simpson and R. Donald Teare. He was a much later starter than they had been but he quickly began to make up for lost time.

His experience of maternity wards in Essex hospitals had made him aware of the rapid spread of streptococcal infection at a time when little was known about the sepsis caused by streptococci or indeed about their identification. This seemed to Camps to be a fruitful field for research and he began to spend as much time as

11

he could at the Ministry of Health laboratory in Endell Street, near Shaftesbury Avenue, London, learning the technique of streptococcal typing.

The raw material for his experiments was obtained for him by a friend from the throats of boys at the well-known public school, Felsted, where his friend was medical officer. But his pathological work in the Essex towns and villages, which was the foundation of his interest in forensic medicine, was increasing all the time and the Essex police relied more and more on his expert advice in the plentiful criminal cases they handled. Competition for that sort of work was lively, but Camps gradually established his reputation as the leading pathologist in the county.

A few years later, Camps was to become honorary consultant pathologist to the British army, but although he was in line for an important army appointment in the Middle East during the war he was turned down on the grounds that he was not fit enough. His war work was largely as consultant pathologist to the Emergency Medical Services. He continued his day-to-day work at Chelmsford throughout the war under Professor S. P. Bedson, a sector pathologist. The two men became close friends and their common interest in forensic science led later to the formation of the British Academy for Forensic Sciences in 1959, of which he became both secretary-general and president. Camps had been one of the original founders of the British Association of Forensic Medicine in 1950 and president from 1958-60.

When more settled conditions were established after the war, Camps began the 'empire-building' for which he was to become somewhat notorious at the London Hospital. His requests were always modest to begin with. In the case of the Chelmsford and Essex Hospital, he started with a former bootroom as his laboratory, with a lad to help him. In due course, he acquired a suite of rooms which were properly and expensively fitted out, and a number of technicians to cope with the increasing amount of work coming to him. All his life, Camps was able to persuade rich men and firms with an interest in the medical world to give money and equipment to help the projects which he originated or was interested in.

Forensic medicine brought fame, and to some extent fortune, to Camps, and he achieved it largely by channelling his activities through the London Hospital itself and its medical college. It was generally considered, even by some of those who became his enemies, that he had built up a forensic medicine department which was the finest in the world. He had started off by leasing, with the approval of the hospital authorities, the building which had been the Hackney mortuary in East London for new chemistry and serological departments. This soon became inadequate, but by the time this happened he had influential friends in the London Hospital hierarchy, one of whom was Professor Richard J. Harrison, F.R.S., now head of the Cambridge University Anatomy School.

The two men had taken an immediate liking for each other when they met and their professional friendship soon became personal as well. Camps had no room of his own in the main building of the hospital and had to make do with a corner in one of the anatomy department's corridors. 'We got Francis a room immediately below mine and it was not long before he was always coming up to see me about his work,' recalls Professor Harrison. 'Whatever I was doing, he would brush it aside humorously, as of no importance. I was also able to help him to get staff.' Camps climbed the promotion ladder steadily. From being lecturer in 1945, he became reader in 1954 and, finally, professor in 1963.

From 1953 onwards, while still a lecturer, Camps' 'team', as he was fond of calling his staff, numbered more than twenty people, including five pathologists, two chemists, two serologists dealing with blood-grouping, saliva and secretion tests, a dentist and a photographer. His chief assistants later were Dr A. C. 'Bill' Hunt, formerly of Bristol and now a well-known pathologist at Plymouth General Hospital, and Dr Hugh Johnson, the present head of the Department of Forensic Medicine at St Thomas's Hospital, London.

Those who worked for Camps at that time were by no means fulsome in their praise of him. It was not a happy department and overwork caused a fair amount of illness among the staff. The public image Camps had been sedulously trying to build up over the years was that of a big-hearted, absent-minded giant, working in a mysterious world that laymen could never fully comprehend, yet at the same time a worldly hedonist who enjoyed life as much as he also enjoyed probing into death. He liked to think of himself as an English medical Maigret and, consciously or unconsciously, copied the mannerisms of the actor Rupert Davies. If when he entered a restaurant – it would always be one of the best – the other diners nudged each other and pointed, his meal was made.

In his own department he could be a bully, according to some of those closest to him. As he became older, he became more rigid in his ideas, cantankerous, despotic even. He was capable of behaving churlishly. It seemed to give him pleasure to feel and see that people were afraid of him. He had an exaggerated view of his own importance in his relationships with other people. Once doctors and others had worked in his department, he regarded it as a betrayal when they left to better themselves – though there was no prospect of advancement in working for him. Dr Hugh Johnson, after years with Camps, incurred his displeasure by taking the St Thomas's appointment. They often met in the company of other doctors but it never ever occurred to Camps to ask how Johnson's department was going, or what his problems were.

One of his associates for many years summed him up by saying that he constantly used people unscrupulously. 'It was one of his least attractive traits,' said his former colleague. 'He did not care whom he alienated. In the end, he drove himself to destruction and everybody else around him. People stayed with him because the opportunities for learning in his department were unique, not because they liked him. He enjoyed power and prestige and was not interested in money. He made money and spent it generously. But people, as such, did not really matter to him.'

Eminent men who had been his friends for years suffered with the rest. Dr Gavin Thurston, the famous Westminster coroner, had been on friendly terms with Camps for many years. They used each other's Christian names, often dined together, and went to the same public dinners and meetings. Camps had entertained Thurston for weekends at his Essex home at Purleigh, a squarely built, former market gardener's house with six acres of ground – Camps always said that when he retired he would grow gladioli there commercially.

For some reason, which Thurston never fathomed, the smiles and jovial quips with which Camps had always greeted him suddenly began to vanish. Many people said during Camps' lifetime that he never grew up, and after the 'quarrel that never was' with Thurston, Camps demonstrated it in a juvenile manner. At meetings and social occasions he would try to edge Thurston away from important guests, and would go to the lengths of standing in front of him or putting up his arm with elbow crooked up to his head in such a way that it obscured him from the rest of the room. In various other ways, he made it plain that as far as he was concerned Thurston did not count.

Camps could behave even worse. When Camps retired, about fifty of his friends and professional colleagues gave him a dinner in the City at the Innholders' Hall. Some years before, professional jealousy had caused a breach of the good relations which had previously existed between Camps and another famous pathologist. Needless to say, the other pathologist declined to attend the dinner. In his absence, Camps decided to attack his former friend. In his speech, his face growing redder and redder with anger, he made no attempt to thank his friends for generously honouring him but launched into a vitriolic tirade against what he called 'some types of pathologist'. It needed no imagination for everybody present to realize whom Camps was attacking. What should have been a pleasant event broke up prematurely amid rumbles of disapproval at his behaviour.

A letter I had recently from an eminent pathologist spoke of the fact that although Camps reached top levels in his profession and undoubtedly had both ability and immense enthusiasm for his job he never managed to gain the affection of his colleagues. Even his fellow pathologists failed to – or refused to – elect him to their governing body, the Council of the College of Pathologists. 'If you are set to write a eulogy that deliberately avoids criticisms – a portrait without warts – you will not create the man so many of us knew,' he wrote. 'He could be affable and likeable in one profile, while planning the contrary attitude in the other. It became very difficult for his friends, both at home and abroad, to accept the rebuffs he handed out so quixotically ... Francis has treated so many of his older friends so badly – so often – that de mortuis nil nisi bonum would be too much for them to swallow.'

Camps could behave in a most devious manner. Mr David Napley, a well-known solicitor and an important figure in the medico-legal world, was his best friend and handled all his legal work for many years. But after Camps' death, he discovered that his services had been dispensed with. A new solicitor had made a new will – Francis Camps actually left £40,000 – and Camps had not said a word to Napley.

Camps could be one of the most charming of men when it suited him but the lowly, as much as the well-known, came in for the snubs he distributed so liberally. A middle-aged woman general practitioner who attended a BMA symposium on sudden death listened with respect as Camps spoke about acute inflammation of the epiglottis in children. It was an esoteric subject, and as the condition is rarely seen the woman doctor asked mildly how she would recognize a case. Camps replied in terms that implied that he regarded the woman as a half-wit. He may have thought he was being clever but the disapproving silence in which his remarks were received would have made a more sensitive man feel otherwise.

Probably to bolster his own ego, because he was well aware of his limitations in many specialist fields, Camps would often administer stinging rebukes to his staff in the presence of others. Dr Barbara Dodd joined Camps, at his urgent request, as a blood-grouping specialist. She was in the blood transfusion service and Camps told her he was trying to build up a forensic science department at the London Hospital especially on the academic side. He said he wanted one or two people who would not have to undertake time-consuming work like paternity tests and attending the mortuaries for ordinary post mortems. He wanted them to concentrate on research and laboratory work (in spite of the honeyed words, the exacting routine mortuary work was to continue), and Dr Dodd, as a leading specialist, would fill this niche and represent the blood-grouping world at top level. In addition, though he did not say it, he would be able to offer facilities to others if he had a first-class department, and this would add to his prestige. Camps spoke warmly of her work, and said he had heard about the book she was writing and would be glad to sponsor it. It was a good start. Later Dr Dodd was to say that Camps was a great character but ...

Dr Dodd soon came to take the view that Camps was a very emotional and insecure man. His insecurity found some expression in his bouts of rudeness.

An example occurred when an important visitor from Switzerland was being entertained at the London Hospital and Camps announced that he would like the senior members of his department to meet him. The meeting took place after lunch in Camps' room and he took the chair. Camps was called out of the room some time later to do an urgent post mortem but was back in half an hour. If this had happened to any one else at such a meeting, Camps would never have thought of filling the person in on what had happened while he was away. On the contrary, he would have taken special delight in being able to keep the person in the dark. But, because Camps always liked to lead every conversation in which he joined, and to take it into the channel he chose, he thought Dr Dodd had slighted him. It was, she admitted, a mistake. Instead of jumping up when Camps returned and telling him of the progress they had made, she allowed the meeting to continue. A few minutes later, when it was too late to recapitulate, she realized from Camps' expression that a storm was about to break and knew it would be over her head because she was the senior doctor present. When Camps got command of the conversation again, he immediately broached a topic vaguely associated with what they had been discussing. Dr Dodd became the target for Camps' professional abuse and everybody at the meeting was aghast. It was an experience she remembered for a very long time.

Part of Camps' trouble was that in his feverish life every minute of his day had to be utilized. He was a restless, dynamic person, brimming with energy, though his staff did not always get the help they should have had from him. He was, however, always quick to give credit where it was due. 'Hugh Johnson and "Taffy" Cameron are far better pathologists than I am,' he would often say when he found they had done a particularly brilliant piece of work.

Much of his value to the department at the London Hospital arose from the fact that he knew how to get in touch with experts for special jobs. It was no use his staff asking for his own expert advice because he never regarded himself as an expert in any particular field. But if he was interested he could be most helpful. He played hard to get but his day was so packed that he *was* hard to get. People would try to waylay him while he was on the way to or from his laboratory. He moved quickly and they would trot by his side, listening eagerly to the words he tossed out of the corner of his mouth while he continued to smoke his pipe. He would continue to talk when he had been picked up by his car and his listener might find himself in the car and miles from where he had started. One secretary once found Camps had rushed into an old-fashioned lift and was descending to the basement while she had to lie flat on the floor near the lift shaft to catch instructions he shouted up to her.

In many ways Camps was a visionary. For instance, he was interested in the medical problems of drug addiction, alcoholism and battered babies long before the subjects became fashionable. He thought big. He worked harder, faster and longer than most of those in the hard-working medical profession. He did not trouble in his early days about eating and sleeping, except to keep himself alive. His view was that time could be better spent.

Inevitably Camps paid, with the greatest reluctance, for this reckless expenditure of his energy. When he was over sixty, he could not bring himself to believe that the amount of work he did at forty was beginning to be beyond his capacity. Physically his system simply could not take it. He was in the position of a man driving a car with the clutch slipping badly. He was over the top of the hill and on the downward slope of the other side while others, who had been less prodigal with their gifts, remained on the pinnacle. He was in the same tragic position that Sir Bernard Spilsbury had found himself in.

It would have been better for Camps if he had been able to relax more than he did but he was not the sort of man who could sit in a deck chair on the beach at Bognor and drowse the afternoon away with a book. He was fond of fly-fishing but seldom had enough leisure for it. He seldom read anything in the newspapers except the headlines and, apart from medical literature, he read hardly anything else. He was too restless to enjoy serious plays but was fond of variety shows and knew a number of music hall favourites, mainly through his club, the Savage, where on late-night convivial occasions, he joined Lord Chief Justice Goddard in lusty sea-shanties.

When he was invited to appear on the BBC's popular programme 'Desert Island Discs', he said most of the records he would have taken with him for a castaway's existence would have been from Noel Coward's shows and similar entertainments such as *Irma La Douce*. For real relaxation, he much preferred going to parties, especially if they were attended by the top people in the police, the legal and medical professions and the scientific world. With a glass of gin in his hand and his pipe well alight, he could ride his favourite hobby horse, which was the importance of forensic medicine, and preface his pontifical statements with his two favourite phrases: 'What you people don't understand ...' and 'We must get on ...'

A colleague who knew Camps as well as anyone once said to me that nobody ever got the key to Camps' character unless they realized that at heart he was a very insecure person. This might have seemed rather far-fetched to those who had to contend with his less likeable and more aggressive traits, and who had experience of his great powers of organization, but it may have been accurate. It was possibly the reason why he deliberately adopted a policy of always drawing around him specialists who knew more about the things in which he was interested. This was mostly obvious to those who were concerned with the day-to-day work of his department than to outsiders. Camps liked an audience and would never give an interview on his own if he could help it. Partly this trait probably stemmed from his realization that the men who had been in pathology all their lives must know more than he did. He was always afraid of being driven into a corner and having to give an opinion when he was not a complete master of the subject. One of the consequences was that members of his staff would go to him for advice and come away bemused by his barrage of talk about things that had no bearing on the subject that ought to have been discussed. Sometimes the unfortunate member of his staff had no time left at all to bring up the subject. When the period allotted for the interview was over, Camps would gather up his papers and be in the process of sweeping out of the room. With his customary 'Good-bye, God bless ...' he would be gone, almost before the staff member realized he was not there.

Francis Camps was a good pathologist – indeed one of the best – but it seemed to those around him that he had not the slightest idea what psychology, which was a very different subject, was all about. He misjudged the characters of those whom he had known for a lifetime. One colleague confessed that Camps seemed to be afraid of her, but she said she was actually timid. Although, with good reason, he had a reputation as a ladies' man, his professional views on women were old-fashioned and dated from his days as a medical student. Women, he thought, in his heart of hearts should really have no place in the rough and tumble of medical life, although he accepted that they were there to stay.

There were two things in his professional life that he cared for above everything. One was forensic medicine, the branch he had chosen and to which he devoted so much time and energy. The other was the young – the medical students and young doctors he had trained and to whom he became an almost God-like figure.

It seemed to many of his colleagues in forensic medicine that he laboured the point a little too much when he continually emphasized the importance of forensic medicine. But it was his life's work to transform a somewhat neglected branch of medicine into one of great importance. The Academy remains as his memorial. With his friend Sir Bentley Purchase, he came to dominate the forensic science world in North London and elsewhere. Camps' young followers were not spared in the interest of the cause. He sent them out all over the country to lecture to medical and medico-legal societies. 'This speciality [forensic medicine] must be recognized,' he preached constantly. 'We must all band together to achieve our object. Those who oppose us or do not help are scabs and bandits.' Strong words, but Camps thought they were true.

Camps sincerely believed in his crusade and travelled thousands of miles, chiefly in America but also in Europe and Africa, to proclaim its importance by lecture and example. He always stayed with the most important medical men as a guest, and when his disciples followed him they were also welcomed as lecturers and guests in places where Camps had been a pioneer.

As a rebel against the 'establishment' Camps was revered by students. He joined in their hobbies and understood their ways of thinking. He had been a hockey player in his youth, and when he became president of the London Hospital club he was not merely a figurehead. Whenever it was possible, he was to be found on the touch-line, cheering on the club.

At the end of the day, Camps had achieved a notable record of public service. He had been a member of many special Home Office, Ministries of Health and Housing and British Medical Association committees, as well as director of the laboratories of the Royal Institute of Public Health and Hygiene from 1960-62. In his extensive library his most prized book was a bound volume of his own published papers and articles, including an important study on the establishment of the time of death and on the identification of human bloodstains. His literary output, as distinct from his ephemeral journalism, was not large and his most impressive book was the second edition of Gradhwol's *Legal Medicine*, which won him the Swiney Prize in 1969 for the best publication of the year on jurisprudence. Camps and Purchase edited the previous edition but the experts thought it was not as comprehensive as it might have been.

On his retirement in 1970, Camps was reported to be contemplating a biography of Sir Bernard Spilsbury, but it would have been superfluous. Spilsbury's definitive biography by D. G. Browne and E. V. Tullett was considered by the critics to be first-rate when it was published in 1951. Purchase himself wrote the foreword.

In the closing years of his career, Camps lectured in forensic medicine at the Royal Free Hospital Medical School, as well as the Middlesex Hospital and University College Hospital. He examined in the medical faculties of no fewer than five British universities. The successful establishment of the diplomas of Medical Jurisprudence was largely due to him and is greatly valued by police surgeons. As editor, he produced the balanced and authoritative journal *Medicine, Science and the Law*, the organ of the British Academy of Forensic Science. Camps was a power in the Medico-Legal Society but his contributions to the society's debates were too diffuse to be really effective and those in charge often had difficulty in persuading him to sit down after he had held the floor for an inordinate time.

The American scene in forensic medicine was familiar to him and at one time he was tempted to accept a post at Harvard. He became a member of the New York Academy of Sciences. A travelling scholarship from the Kellogg Foundation helped to satisfy his urge to journey frequently across the Atlantic.

Camps was one of the first to realize the value of television for publicizing forensic medicine. Years before, the voice of Dr Charles (later Lord) Hill had become famous as that of the first 'radio doctor'. The bland face of Camps was known to wide audiences as the 'television doctor' by the time he died. His programme on the Setty case was masterly and he showed none of the traces of nervousness which often spoilt his appearances on lecture platforms.

Camps was flattered by the attentions of the top men in the television world. He gave them the run of his department, even though it upset routine working, and he was always ready for awkward questions. A television man who burst into his room waving a human bone was given an answer when he asked: 'Could we do a blood-grouping on this bone after so many years?'

A factual programme entitled 'The Hidden Truth', illustrating the way in which forensic scientists worked, was pronounced to be first-rate television material. Another programme called 'The Great Professor Makes a Mistake' was based on a mistake Camps had actually made himself when, like the fictionalized television professor, he was worn out after a hard day's work. Camps also advised on television fiction and his staff joked among themselves that he had become so engrossed in this that, in the end, he did not know whether he was dealing with reality or fiction.

Francis Camps, who married three times, was a great family man, although he had little time in his busy life to devote to his wives and children. His first wife was a nurse whom he met when he was a doctor at Guy's Hospital; when the marriage ended in divorce, she went to Canada. His second wife, 'Bunny', was a frail, diffident 'little woman' type, whose nervous ways seemed to appeal to strong masculine men. Her appearance was deceptive. She was actually a highly skilled pathologist, whom Camps had met while working at Harold Wood in Essex. She died in America. Camps married his third wife a few months before he died.

After Camps' retirement his health deteriorated badly and his last months were clouded by illness and pain, which he attempted, not entirely successfully, to smother with drugs. His retirement in 1970 was only partial and he remained almost as busy as ever. His zest for life was undiminished. Sir Frederick (Lord Justice) Lawton was one of many friends at a party at his flat in Barbican, London, where Camps talked amusingly and, as usual, incessantly. 'Although I knew him well I had no reason to think from anything he said that he knew he was reaching the end of his journey through life,' said Sir Frederick Lawton.

But Camps did know, and it is tragic to think that he was to die, not from the disease that he thought had gripped him, but from one which could have been cured if it had been treated. Camps believed that the intense pains in his abdomen were caused by cancer. He had never been ill and could not understand sickness in others. He genuinely did not understand people who stayed away from work because they were ill. When his final illness was on him, he had no patience with himself and certainly did not feel self-pity. He was terrified of doctors and thought he did not need a doctor to tell him he had the particular type of cancer he thought he had, and which he knew was not very susceptible to surgical treatment. He became extremely thin and reached the conclusion, quite cold-bloodedly, that an operation would not be worth all the trouble, pain, inconvenience and expense it would entail; he thought that in any case it was unlikely the operation would be successful.

He had a premonition that he was dying. A few days before his death on 8 July 1972, he rang up a close friend and said to her: 'This time next week, you will be at my funeral.' He was right to the day. He decided to let the 'cancer' take its course.

He was not a hypochondriac but during an earlier part of his life he had become convinced that he had tuberculosis. An X-ray would have told him that he had not, but it took a long time and probably caused him a great deal of misery before he convinced himself that he had grown out of it. When he finally collapsed at the end of his life with what he thought was cancer, he was rushed to hospital and had an emergency operation. The cancer was non-existent. He had a stomach ulcer which would have yielded to treatment. Consequently if he had behaved rationally, he would have had a few more years of life.

In the medical press his friends paid handsome tributes to him. 'He was such a personality that he could and did enlist the help of an uncountable number of experts to help him in some aspects of his work. He was a good witness but tended to take sides and, to the purist, he was not an ideal witness. All the same he never allowed his interest in one side of the case to prevent the most exhaustive investigation of all the facts. In court, he would present them carefully and completely,' wrote Dr H. B. May, an old friend.

Dr May concluded that in retirement Camps was looking forward to continuing his work and advancing his subject in foreign countries with less well-developed departments than his own at the London Hospital. 'He was an outstanding forensic expert and a good friend; and a scrupulously fair adversary in the courts,' he wrote.

In the *British Medical Journal*, an editorial obituary notice described him as a delightful host and guest, having a rich fund of humour. He was a member of both the Savage and Savile clubs, a former hockey player and for many years, president of the London Hospital hockey club; fishing was his main recreation. 'F.E.C. was a very loyal and devoted friend and stimulating colleague,' said the writer. 'He loved life and it is a tragedy that his was cut short at a time when he had still so much to contribute to forensic medicine and when he had only just begun to enjoy his semi-retirement.'

The Lancet said he was a rebel against establishment order; he had hung, on two opposite walls in his small laboratory, framed, illuminated mottoes stating: 'It has always been done like this', and 'It has never been done before'. 'He had unlimited energy and smoked fifty cigarettes a day especially in the laboratory, despite the warnings of Hill and Doll,' wrote 'R.D.G.'. 'He was a marvellous tutor and mentor to his juniors and he was so mature in those days that it is difficult for me to believe that he was only five years older than me.'

Even as death was approaching, Camps could not forget some of the obsessions that for some years had taken over from his common sense. For example, his greatest fear in later life was that Professor Keith Simpson, whom he regarded as an enemy, would eventually perform a post mortem examination on him. This, of course, was nonsense. It is doubtful whether the professor would have accepted instructions to do so but the situation did not arise. Camps died outside the area in which Simpson normally worked. In any case, he died what is normally judged to be a natural death and no post mortem was necessary.

In the Mortuary

Every pathologist differs in his approach to his work. In even the most modern mortuary the smell is nauseating. A young policeman who was on duty when the great Sir Bernard Spilsbury was performing a post mortem sought to dilute it and quieten his queasy stomach by lighting a cigarette. Spilsbury immediately asked him to put the cigarette out. 'If you smoke I cannot smell what I want to smell,' he said.

Camps was different. Not only did he smoke incessantly while he was working, dropping ash all over the place, but his secretary was often requested to put a cigarette in his mouth and light it. His fingers became yellow and his lips were stained with nicotine. Some of the wives of his friends thought his appearance repulsive. A pathologist has been described as a surgeon of the dead and, as such, should observe the hygienic rules of surgery. Camps ignored them. He would never wear a mask to avoid blood or fluid splashes and declined to wear the surgical boots that mortuary attendants pressed on him – if they did not know him. He often rushed into a mortuary, performed a post mortem in his ordinary clothes, and rushed out. At a post mortem at which he was assisted by Frederick Oughton, the mortuary technician, Camps ripped a rubber glove while opening a rib cage and caused a scratch which bled. Most pathologists, aware of the danger of septicaemia, would have had the scratch treated immediately, as Oughton urged. Not Camps. He refused the offer of a new glove and continued the post mortem. 'I used to do autopsies with bare hands,' he said.

In the mortuary Camps has been described as a 'navvy' by some technicians who worked for him. They did not think he was an elegant operator. But no one denied that he was quick. In the picturesque words of Dr Hugh Johnson, 'he would pass through a mortuary like fire through a cornfield'. In his personal relations with those around him, he frequently trod on toes. He had a lordly disregard for protocol, which plays an important part in hospital life. If he was engaged to perform a post mortem at a hospital, he did not often trouble to pay the courtesy call expected by the head of department concerned. Camps one day arrived unexpectedly for a post mortem, as he often did, and the technician deputed to work with him suggested that he should telephone the departmental head to let him know that Camps had arrived. 'Don't bother,' was the brusque reply.

To those under him, he was not over-generous with money, although he made a very comfortable income, but this was probably part of his own deliberate build-up of himself as a 'character', because he never spared expense when he was entertaining, either at home or in restaurants. He was generous, also, to his senior staff on their birthdays and at Christmas. Before the war pathologists were poorly paid, but in postwar years the London County Council produced a schedule of fees which enabled a full-time pathologist to become reasonably well-off. The fee for a post mortem and report went up from £3 to £7.50 and for an examination and evidence from £5 to £12, but, in many cases, this was only the beginning. There were extra fees for analyses of various sorts and for opinions. Camps was usually called in as an expert for the defence and in important cases, especially those in the civil courts where a great deal of money might be involved, he could command £300 for a conference and court appearance. His salary as a Home Office pathologist of about £1,500 was only the beginning. Yet he cultivated a reputation for meanness. He would never, for instance, leave the usual £1 tip for the technicians or mortuary keepers who did the donkey work at a post mortem, although he expected far more to be done for him than most other pathologists. There would be black looks for everyone if the body was not prepared exactly as he expected it. This included opening it up and removing organs for his inspection, which strictly speaking was the work the pathologist should have done himself.

Camps was reputed in forensic circles to have no sense of humour, or, if he had, it was macabre, but this was not quite accurate. Dr R. A. K. Clarke, who trained at the London Hospital in Camps' time and is now in practice at Erith, Kent, remembers inviting Camps to lecture to the Medical Society, the senior undergraduate society at the London Hospital, on a subject of his own choice. Dr Clarke describes Camps' sense of humour more as 'wicked' and says that when Camps discovered that the night of the talk was to be General Election night, he said the choice of a title was obvious: 'Exhuma-

26

tion.' 'Sure enough,' says Dr Clarke, 'Sir Alec lost the election! All in all he was one of the friendliest men I have ever met.'

As a lecturer Camps was not first-class. In a conference about a case in which he had been retained, he bubbled with enthusiasm and was full of ideas about how the case ought to be developed. But when he stood on a platform, he seemed totally unable to communicate his ideas to his audience, even to medical students, with whom as I have said he was very popular. He had no tricks or gimmicks. Professor Donald Teare used to sharpen the interest of his audience by beginning: 'This afternoon, I am going to lecture on a subject that will interest all of you – rape.' His listeners would brighten and Teare would shuffle his papers. 'Ah, no. I was wrong. My subject I see is "Staining".' But Teare had secured the attention of his audience and his more technical lecture would be a great success. Professor Keith Simpson had a similar technique. 'Well,' he would say, 'You have only come to see my dirty pictures, so let's get on with them!'

But Camps, according to Lord Justice Lawton, was not a good lecturer. He did not project the main issues of his lectures successfully. He was deflected by any side issues that took his fancy. Nevertheless, some of his students remember how informative his lectures were, especially those illustrated by slides, although it was not uncommon for Camps to mix up his slides and claim, for instance, that he was showing one which illustrated a piece of a lymphatic gland when it was really a section of a lung. 'His methods were a pleasure to watch and learn from,' wrote Dr P. R. Stevens, now of Blackburn, 'as each case history unfolded and his findings found their correct place in the solution of the problem, with a logical inevitability that delighted the understanding.'

Spilsbury, in his busiest days at the end of the thirties, performed 700 to 1,000 post mortems a year and used to explain that a pathologist might possibly do 1,100 to 1,200 but no more. Camps proved that this was not necessarily so. With his streamlined technique, he could complete a post mortem in ten minutes, providing the police or other doctors had given him a general idea what to look for. Starting without much prior knowledge of the cadaver on the slab, a post mortem might have taken him an hour. Taking the difficult autopsies with the easy ones, it was estimated that he would work his way through 45 a week for 46 weeks of the year – perhaps roughly a total of two thousand. In his later years he travelled frequently to America, the Middle East and Africa to lecture and demonstrate post mortems and the number he performed was not so large. But he himself estimated in 1956 that he had performed about 60,000 post mortems, and from 1956 until he retired he must have added a further 28,000. When I talked to Professor Donald Teare in 1973, he had done 88,000 and was five years away from retirement. Camps' score was prodigious, but even his record will almost certainly be beaten by Teare.

Spilsbury did all his own preparations when he conducted post mortems. He had his own 'tools', as he called his surgical instruments, which he carried everywhere, and he made out his case cards in his own crabbed, almost illegible handwriting. When Camps performed post mortems in hospitals other than the London, he strolled into the post mortem room with his hands in his pockets and merely called for a set of instruments – any instruments. He almost invariably 'borrowed' test tubes, bottles and other receptacles for specimens he took from the body. To the annoyance of the hospital technicians, he hardly ever troubled to return what he had 'borrowed'.

Unlike Spilsbury, Camps never wrote out his own post mortem reports. His method was to have his secretary in the mortuary behind a screen or in an adjoining room and dictate to her as he worked. As he was often demonstrating to students as he performed his autopsies, he used two tones of voice. In one tone he would tell students what he was doing and why, and in the other he would dictate to his secretary what he wished to be included in his post mortem report.

He worked at phenomenal speed and, as he had an extraordinarily good memory, he would often dictate his report on one corpse while actually working on the next. The results seemed bizarre to onlookers. 'It was very disconcerting to those who did not know his ways to hear him dictate that he was examining the body of a well-nourished female when actually he was examining the body of an old man,' says Dr I. M. Librach, now of Chadwell Heath Hospital.

Another incident of this kind occurred at Joyce Green Hospital,

Dartford. A child from a nearby gypsy encampment was admitted moribund from gastro-enteritis and died within an hour or so of admission. The case was reported to the coroner, who ordered a post mortem. 'It was arranged for 2.30 p.m. the following afternoon,' reports Dr Michael C. Gill-Carey, now of St Agnes, Cornwall. 'Unfortunately an emergency admission delayed my attendance and I arrived at the mortuary some ten minutes late. Francis Camps had almost finished the examination and was dictating to his secretary "fractures of the left 4th, 5th and 6th ribs, undershaft fracture of the left humerus, depressed fracture of the left parietal".

'I suppose,' writes Dr Gill-Carey, 'that as he dictated this, the expression on my face must have indicated amazement and some alarm at having missed the diagnosis of all these injuries, for Francis Camps glanced up at me and said "Oh, it's quite all right, doctor. It's simple gastro-enteritis. I am dictating about another post mortem!"'

Dr Gill-Carey said he had never met Camps before. 'I was impressed that he immediately sized up what was going through my mind and instantly reassured me. I discovered later that it was his habit to do post mortems, keeping the details in his mind until his secretary appeared, when he might dictate the findings of two or three previous ones while performing another. The clarity of his brain was such that the details remained unentangled and ready for the dictation.'

Dr Gill-Carey met Camps several years later when he had gone into general practice at St Agnes. A local publican's daughter had been killed by her lover as a result of two shots fired at close range from an automatic pistol.

'It was widely held that this was murder,' says Dr Gill-Carey. 'But at the trial, Camps appeared for the defence. His erudition and obvious expertise in the forensic medical field, with special reference to this case of firearms, convinced the jury that the accused's defence might well be correct.

'He had stated that the girl was threatening to leave him. He had come with the gun to try and persuade her to remain or he would shoot himself. She had tried to wrest the gun from him and it had gone off.

'How then to explain the second shot? Camps demonstrated that the gun had a very light trigger action and that when fired, the recoil of the gun was sufficient at times to press the finger on the trigger, firing it again. He explained that the first shot entered the girl's abdomen in a somewhat downward direction. She would then have released her grip, allowing her lover's hand to fly up, at the same time accidentally firing the second shot, which hit her in the head. The man was acquitted of murder and a verdict of manslaughter was brought in.'

Dr Ann Peach, now a London doctor, remembers how Camps cleared up what was at first a puzzling case at a hospital in Farnborough, Kent. The patient, subsequently a corpse, a mother of two children, was admitted seriously ill from a throat infection thought to be tetanus. There was no sign of a scratch or bleeding and the woman, whose husband knew she was pregnant, had not been unduly worried. The pregnancy was apparently running its normal course.

But the woman died and at the post mortem Camps made the surprising discovery that the woman had tried to abort herself, using the old back street abortionist's remedy – slippery elm. The woman had been examined by the hospital doctors but they had not noticed the self-abortion.

When Camps was due to lecture at the Farnborough hospital, all the housemen and medical students, whether attending the lecture or not, would crowd at the windows. They were not, however, exclusively interested in Camps, but also in the attractive 'dolly birds' who seemed to go with him whenever he visited hospitals!

Dr Peach recalls nostalgically Camps' habit of rushing into a post mortem room and beginning a post mortem without troubling to take off his coat. A 'simple' post mortem would take him an average of ten minutes but if something baffled him he would take up to two hours to complete it.

In spite of his apparent casualness, as Mr Oughton also recalled, Camps could be a martinet. He expected everything to be ready for him and his snappy demands for 'bottle 1', 'bottle 2', 'test tube 1' and so on were made in a tone of voice that caused his technicians to move swiftly.

Although many of Camps' swans were geese, and his enthusiasms for causes and types of research in which he was interested had a way of petering out, he had an infinite capacity for inspiring all kinds of people with his own enthusiasms. In his own department at the London Hospital, his enthusiasms were quickly communicated, but people who knew him well would tend to play them down among themselves. They had seen it all happen too often before. But because of his own enthusiasm for forensic medicine, young doctors who came under his influence at the London Hospital invariably became great believers in it, even though, in those early days, forensic medicine was often described as the poor relation of medicine.

An example of the way his enthusiasm was generated among others occurred when Camps and a friend were discussing the future of the friend's son. The son had been wondering whether the life of a doctor would suit him and Camps generously suggested that he would take on the young man as a laboratory assistant for a month to see whether he might like it. It would, said Camps, give him a chance at least to see what it was all about. The young man accepted the offer eagerly and worked with Camps at Hackney mortuary for a month.

Camps aroused his interest but, after reflection, the young man decided he was not really cut out to be a doctor. He chose to try to become a regular soldier and went before a War Office selection board for an interview, at which one of the tests was to give a ten minute lecture on a subject of his own choice. He announced that he would speak on 'A day in the work at Hackney mortuary'. Eyebrows twitched at the choice, but by the time he had finished the members of the selection board were leaning forward with interest. There should have been no questions and the next cadet was ready for his turn, but the examiners began to ask questions about this intriguing subject. It was twenty minutes later before the president of the board realized what was happening and the next cadet was called in. Such was the interest aroused by Camps in a youngster who was not even going on with the project of becoming a doctor.

The gap between the specialist knowledge of a Home Office pathologist such as Francis Camps and that of the general practitioner dealing daily with the painful minor ailments, is very wide. That between the pathologist and the full-time police surgeon accustomed to examining the bodies of people who have died violently is still wide enough to be noticeable. A police surgeon does not work in what Camps has described as the 'palace of truth'. He has to take things as he finds them and they are often rough and unpleasant. He is usually the first specialist in the field and it is not surprising that sometimes his diagnosis does not match the facts when they are all brought into the open.

Dr David Matthews, a North London police surgeon of many years' standing, on several occasions had the experience of preceding the redoubtable Camps to the scene of a crime. They were on friendly terms and Matthews, with the help of his uniformed police colleagues, was often able to show Camps the short cuts. Camps was always courteous and considerate to his professional colleagues who had not acquired his deep knowledge of forensic medicine and who often stood in some awe of him.

One case in which both doctors were concerned was, on the face of it, ordinary and straightforward. A man taking a short cut to his work through a field near Elstree saw a youngish man under a hedge, apparently asleep. It was a warm July morning and the heavy dew must have given the man a soaking but did not seem to disturb his slumber. The workman took the same route home and was surprised to see the man still asleep. But he took a closer look and saw that the man was not asleep but dead.

Dr Matthews arrived as soon as he could, looked at the body and informed Detective-Inspector Peter Gill that he did not think the man's death had been violent. There were no external injuries and the ground nearby did not seem to have been disturbed. The police surgeon wisely kept to himself any theories he might have had about the cause of death until a post mortem had established it.

In every police force there are men, some of whom have reached senior positions, who always know better than their chiefs – and the doctors. The man's body in this case was moved to the mortuary and there was nothing to stop nosey detectives from taking a look at it. That evening, there was a palaver in the quiet mortuary between over-zealous policemen. The corpse had been undressed by the mortuary keeper in readiness for the post mortem, and talkative detectives took a look. They found bruising, blisters and even a 'fracture'. Word went upwards to higher-ranking police officers, who were greatly displeased at the thought that they had been left behind in a murder hunt because the police surgeon had not been smart enough to spot injuries at his preliminary examination.

As a result of the jitteriness on the part of the senior officers, Camps himself was asked to carry out the post mortem. In the meantime Matthews and Gill drove to the isolated mortuary and had another look at the body. Matthews saw bruises and blisters that had not been there before, but this did not worry him. He knew what the unqualified policemen could not have known – that they formed part of the post-death changes and were natural phenomena. 'We will see what Dr Camps has to say in the morning,' said Matthews. 'I will stick to my original opinion.'

What Camps had to say was brief and to the point. The dead man had not been attacked, he had not been dumped in the field after an accident, and it was not a case of murder, all of which had been mooted by the detectives. He had taken an overdose of barbiturates before he lay down under the hedge for his last sleep and the so-called bruising and blistering was due to after-death staining and the drug over-dose. It was a case of little – or no – knowledge being a nuisance to the doctors.

The Expert Witness

It is widely accepted, as a general statement, that doctors do not make good court witnesses and Camps, in his relentless pursuit of his self-imposed task of improving standards in forensic medicine, constantly preached the importance of presenting evidence clearly and without ambiguity. He derided doctors who tried to blind the courts with science and ended by confusing everybody. Camps thought that, fundamentally, the poor showing of doctors in the witness box was due to a lack of knowledge of court procedure and understanding of the relationship between the law and the expert medical witness. Dr P. R. Stevens, one of Camps' former students, remembers that Professor Camps encouraged them to attend as many types of court as possible to familiarize themselves with court procedure and especially to attend when Camps himself was giving evidence.

The students were usually thrilled and considered their chief's performance flawless, but medico-legal experts had a more critical approach. As I have indicated, they did not consider Camps to be a perfect witness, and one of his own colleagues expressed the view that, basically, the reason was Camps' own sense of insecurity. Lord Justice Lawton, as a Queen's Bench divisional judge, often tried cases in which Camps gave evidence and came to the conclusion that 'he was not all that good in the witness box'. He was good at explaining the fundamental issues at stake in a case at conference or consultation but his limitations in the witness box were soon obvious to experienced counsel. David Napley, president of the Medico-Legal Society and a well-known legal forensic expert who often engaged Camps, found it worrying and dangerous to a case that he would say one thing in private and something quite different in court.

This was countered to some extent by his reputation, but his chief asset as an expert witness was that he knew most experts in the various fields of medicine and could organize medical and scientific evidence better than anybody else.

Camps had a burning desire to see that people had a fair trial and he would go to almost any lengths to help those whom he thought had not. His activities in the case of Dennis Stafford and Michael Luvaglio showed how he would work to prevent what he thought was a miscarriage of justice. Camps was not involved professionally in the case in which the two men were charged at Newcastle with the murder on 1 May 1967 of Angus Stuart Sibbet, a gambling machine owner in the sleazy north-eastern clubland. They were found guilty and sentenced to life imprisonment. Camps took up their case and turned it into a crusade. He found time to give advice whenever those defending the two men asked for it. He carried out technical experiments in his laboratories and travelled hundreds of miles, all in the interests of what he thought was justice. The case almost became an obsession with him, but it turned out to be a waste of time.

In his early days of giving evidence in court as an expert witness, Camps soon appreciated that defences were often severely handicapped because they could not get evidence of the same quality as the Crown. At that time, there was no legal aid and problems of finance usually entered into the picture. Unscrupulous doctors would try to cash in and offer, for a fee, to give evidence.

Camps grew up in a pathological world dominated by Sir Bernard Spilsbury. In Spilsbury's time any accused who had to meet his evidence was hard put to find a pathologist prepared to oppose it. That is why, a generation later, when Camps was established as a leading pathologist himself, he was always willing to appear for the defence, provided that he thought that his own evidence would help. Friends told Camps that he did his reputation no good by appearing constantly for the defence, and said it might be concluded that the reason was that the Crown would not employ him. But Camps appreciated the difficulties in which many defences found themselves and did his best to provide a counter-balance.

One of the reasons why judges with extensive medical knowledge – as many had and have – did not always trust Camps' evidence was that they were not impressed by the depth and extent of his pathological knowledge. There were pathologists with deeper knowledge, such as Teare and Simpson. Judges often thought Camps' evidence bore signs of a quick impression rather than carefully thought out reasoning. But situations were saved because he was, and gave the impression of being, an honest man. He was always ready to admit that the conclusions and theories of the other side were tenable, and his enthusiasm, which often over-influenced his judgment, and his extraordinary energy, outweighed his defects.

An interesting example of the way Camps could organize a case, for either defence or prosecution, occurred in 1967 when Mrs Maureen Audrey Hucks, a twenty-seven-year-old mother of two from Wellington, Somerset, sued a general practitioner, Dr John Hugh Cole. She claimed damages for negligence after contracting fulminating septicaemia following the birth of her third child.

The trouble started in August 1963 when Mrs Hucks' wedding ring finger began to swell and she had the ring filed off. Three small but painful spots were found but Dr Cole did not regard them as serious. The pregnancy continued in the normal way and her baby was born in the local nursing home. But the day after delivery a nurse, while washing Mrs Hucks, noticed red patches on a finger and toe. This was more serious and Dr Cole took the precaution of having a swab sent to a pathological laboratory. In the meantime the doctor had prescribed an antibiotic drug called tetracycline, in tablet form, four times a day. The course of treatment prescribed was completed in five days, after which both finger and toe had nearly healed, and the whole business was regarded as almost trivial.

But it was not. The pathological report stated that a named streptococcus was the cause of the trouble and that it was resistant to tetracycline. Nevertheless, as the sickness seemed to be 'all over bar the shouting', to quote Dr Cole, he gave no further treatment. The day after her discharge from hospital, Mrs Hucks became violently ill and was almost dead when she was re-admitted to hospital. Fortunately she recovered, though she was left with speech and personality problems, as a result of which she brought her action.

The action was based on three grounds. Her counsel said the doctor failed to treat her finger when it was first shown to him, failed to change the antibiotic tetracycline after seeing the laboratory report, and did not renew the course of antibiotics when it was finished.

Experts were still experimenting with antibiotics in the sixties and such knowledge as they had gained had not always percolated down to all general practitioners, especially those in rural districts. The question underlying the action was how much knowledge ought a general practitioner to have.

Camps was retained by Mrs Hucks and he organized a team which consisted of himself, Mr Alec Bourne, the famous gynaecologist, and Dr H. B. May, the eminent biologist. It was the London Hospital against the rest. London's view was that a mistake had been made in not continuing the antibiotic treatment and the court accepted Dr May's evidence that it was wrong to discontinue the treatment of an infection until one was sure that the patient was not at risk. He also expressed the view that organisms on the finger were much more dangerous than organisms elsewhere. A responsible practitioner would make sure that the patient was not at risk until the involution, or curling inwards of the uterus, was complete.

The West Country team mobilized on behalf of Dr Cole was a

strong one and included two pathologists and an obstetrician: 'Obviously,' Mr Justice Lawton said, 'very honest witnesses doing their best to help me in a very difficult case.'

The problem was: had there been negligence? The judge ruled that there had been no negligence in failing to treat the finger or failing to change the antibiotic after seeing the laboratory report but that the doctor was wrong in not continuing the treatment. He rejected the view that consultants were putting far too much responsibility on general practitioners in the handling of antibiotics. 'I found that a general practitioner ought to have a knowledge of antibiotics,' Lord Justice Lawton summed up the case to me, 'and that he was negligent in not having it; or in having it and not using it.' He awarded damages of £2,500, which were increased to £4,000 when the case was taken to appeal.

The decision of the courts aroused concern about the attitude they might adopt in future actions for negligence, commented the authoritative *British Medical Journal*. It said that the standard of skill required of a doctor by the law had been the standard of a doctor of ordinary competence and of equivalent qualifications and pretensions to skill. The Court of Appeal in the present case purported to apply this same standard. Delivering judgment in the Appeal Court, Lord Denning said a charge of professional negligence was serious. It stood on a different footing to a charge of negligence against the driver of a motor car. The consequences were far more serious. It affected his professional status and reputation. The burden of proof was correspondingly greater. As the charge was so grave, so should the proof be clearer.

Lord Denning said a doctor was only liable when he fell below the standard of a reasonably competent practitioner in his field so much so that his conduct might be deserving of censure or inexcusable. The decision, commented the *British Medical Journal*, was unsatisfactory in its application of law to the facts of the case ... It was during this case that a London evening newspaper put out a news-bill which read 'Doctor Camps in Box'.

Another example, perhaps minor but illustrative of the way Francis Camps would help people in trouble and also knew specialists who could do it, arose from an incident at Balham, London.

Late one evening, two Scotsmen who were drink-taken, made a

37

nuisance of themselves in the street and policemen, after watching their antics for some time, decided to arrest them. The police needed neither assistance nor advice from outsiders but a schoolmaster thought they did and followed them to the police station. He began to argue that the arrest was unjustified and made other points. After an angry scene, the police ordered him outside. The schoolmaster had not the sense to clear off and when the Scotsmen were in the cells the police brought the master back into the station and charged him with assaulting a policeman – by spitting at him. A policeman's blue tunic was produced and the schoolmaster was shown a whitish stain on the lapel. He was told it was spittle.

The schoolmaster had influential friends, one of whom was a pathologist who knew Camps and said he would ask for his help. 'They can't do this,' said Camps, ignoring the fact that 'they' had done it. 'They have to show that the stain is saliva and that it comes from the same blood-group as the schoolmaster's. I don't suppose they have thought of that.'

On this occasion, Camps had an expert on his own doorstep – Dr Barbara Dodd, who worked in his laboratory at the London Hospital. It became obvious that the policeman who had arrested the schoolmaster had no idea that saliva belongs to different blood-groups when Dr Dodd showed that the stain was of A group and the schoolmaster's of O group. The police pressed on with the case but when the police forensic tests provided the same results as those of Dr Dodd the magistrate dismissed the case without even calling on Dr Dodd to give evidence.

Camps, by the very nature of his qualities, made enemies as he was bound to do but his friends were legion and as the following pages show, he was an outstanding pathologist whose name became justly famous in his own lifetime.

Two

Three Cases

The Torso in the Essex Marshes

Many epithets have been applied to Brian Donald Hume, a so-called company director from Golders Green, North London, who was tried in January 1950 for the murder of a shady car dealer called Stanley Setty. Hume is said to have been a cold-blooded, avaricious, cunning thief and a plausible liar, who would tell any story if it suited him. His own words in the witness box were that he was 'a semi-honest man'. But the question an Old Bailey jury was asked to decide was not about his honesty but whether he was a murderer. Hume swore he was not and carried such conviction that the jury acquitted him. On the other hand, the judge's manner and words at the trial made it clear that he was on the side of the disbelievers. The judge saw that everything that could be said in favour of Hume was said but, when the second charge of being an accessory to murder by disposing of Setty's body followed the murder acquittal, he gave Hume the severe sentence of twelve years. Hume served as much of his sentence as the law demanded: eight years. He emerged, in the words of a writer who saw a great deal of him during his first free days, a nervous, rebellious, fantastically touchy wreck of a man. This did not prevent Hume from boasting, as soon as he was released from prison, that he had in fact killed Setty, and robbed him of a large sum of money as a sort of afterthought. Which was the truth? Hume was indeed such a liar that if it had been known for certain that he was telling the truth few people would have believed him. But, as we shall see, there was a tragic aftermath of the murder of Stanley Setty, which made it certain that Hume's story that he was a murderer was the true one.

Camps came into the case as the Home Office pathologist who performed the post mortem on the headless, legless, water-sodden body of Setty which arrived in his department at the London Hospital as an untidy bundle. Camps thought at first it must have been thrown over a cliff into the sea and later washed up. 'More likely it's been run over by a steam-roller,' said an assistant, as he surveyed the squashed remains. They were found at Tillington in Essex and Camps' theory was only slightly off-beam. The torso had been flung from a light aircraft into the sea; it was then, as now, a unique method of disposing of a murdered body. In view of the injuries, it was an understandable misjudgment, soon to be corrected when Camps' full post mortem was made.

The case, when it was paraded through the courts, gave a surprised public a glimpse of the unwholesome side of the London secondhand car business which still has its centre around Warren Street, on the north-east edge of Soho.

For many years before the Second World War, Warren Street was one of the sights of London. It was not quite comparable with Petticoat Lane or Club Row in the East End, where the traders were more exotic and the goods bought, sold and exchanged more exciting. Warren Street was a cut above these tumultuous bazaars. The cars they dealt in there were not exactly junk, though many unwary buyers would rue the day they ventured into the area with a pocketful of cash. The origin of many of the cars was suspect. But the glib, well-dressed men who thronged the streets and whose duty, so they averred, was to be the benefactors of the car-hungry public, gave the environment an air of prosperity. There might be receivers of stolen cars among them, or ringers and men who knew how to turn a hire purchase agreement inside out, but they were in a minority. Only those in the know, like the astute young detectives from Tottenham Court Road Police Station, knew that all was not as it seemed to be in Warren Street.

Setty, who was born in Baghdad and originally named Sulman Setty, was a general 'spiv' whose main line of business was stolen cars. Hume worked as a car 'snatcher' for him and as a 'flying smuggler' for himself, claiming that he landed contraband goods at remote, disused airfields. He was a good-looking, loquacious man who was never very affluent and had a chip on his shoulder. According to Christie, the strangler, who was in the remand section of Brixton Prison awaiting trial at the same time as Hume, he had an uncertain temper and had to be 'watched'. The chip arose from an unhappy childhood. Hume said he was illegitimate. He had never known his father, and his mother, a school-teacher, who brought him up in a Dorset village, made him call her 'auntie'. Hume served in the RAF as an aircraftman from the outbreak of war but he never became a pilot because he was hopeless at navigation. He was discharged on health grounds after eighteen months. On leaving the RAF Hume worked for a time in a hotel kitchen but, even there, was thinking of bigger things. There is no doubt that he had an inventive mind and an improved electric toaster which he patented was marketed successfully. His grandiose plans did not often mature and one reason was that he could not always distinguish between fact and fantasy. He was fined for wearing an RAF officer's uniform and other minor misdemeanours. In between acting (he said) as a go-between for British owners of light aircraft and Middle East entrepreneurs who needed them for dubious purposes, he went for a holiday to the little Brecon town of Hay. There he decided to set up a factory to make electrical appliances. He boasted that he would soon be employing at least a hundred people, but the plan never really got off the ground. While he was at Brecon he met Cynthia Wright, the daughter of a local bank manager, and they were married in 1948.

There is no doubt that shortly before Setty's death Hume was very hard up. He had recently raised a few pounds by pawning a suit and a ring. If there was any easy money going, Hume was ready to reach for it with both hands.

There will never be any way of telling exactly how Stanley Setty came to die. When Hume had served his sentence for disposing of Setty's body and, since he had been acquitted of his murder, could not face another murder charge, he gave his own version of what had happened to a Sunday newspaper and was believed to have been paid £10,000 for it. Hume, always a man for exploiting human emotions, said he had originally taken a dislike to Setty when he saw him kick his (Hume's) Alsatian dog, Tony. To the dislike was added suspicion when word reached Hume that Setty was paying too much attention to his wife, Cynthia. Money was also a constant

41

source of friction between Hume and Setty, with Hume claiming that his cut from the stolen car racket was not enough, considering the risks he ran. In the end, said Hume, it was the woman who triggered off the fatal row. Hume, tired and short of money, had returned to his flat on the evening of 4 October 1949 and his temper was not improved by the sight of Setty's Citroën car parked outside. He found Setty lolling on the sofa of the sitting room. (Exactly how Setty got into the flat when Mrs Hume was not there was never explained.)

Hume said he told Setty to get out or be slung out. Setty retorted that Hume would be the one to be slung out, if he tried anything on. Hume admitted that he then lost control of himself. He rushed out to the landing, seized a German dagger which was one of a collection of war souvenirs on the landing wall and returned to the room. From then onwards, the story lost nothing in the telling. Setty, said Hume, was now white with fright, called him a silly bastard and told him to go away. Setty got up to defend himself and in the struggle Hume plunged the dagger frenziedly and repeatedly into his chest and legs, 'wielding it,' wrote Hume with a dramatic touch, 'just like our savage ancestors wielded weapons 20,000 years ago'. Hume said the fight lasted just two minutes. Although the two men had been battling for their lives, Hume had the presence of mind to look at the clock on the wall and note that it was 7.25 p.m. It seems incomprehensible but Hume said the Alsatian dog in the next room slept through what must have been a noisy and terrible struggle.

Setty was physically a big man, 'fat, or very fat', said Mr Christmas (now Judge) Humphreys who prosecuted at the Old Bailey, and Hume must have been exhausted by the brief but strenuous fight. Nevertheless, Hume was able to drag the corpse across the hall and through the dining room. Then he hid it in a big cupboard in the scullery which was used for storing coal.

There was now a fair amount of cleaning up to be done and Hume was cool-headed enough to take a duster and wipe off finger-prints on the furniture so efficiently that the police were unable to find a single print when they searched the flat. He also remembered Setty's car which he had seen parked outside. He found the ignition key in Setty's pocket, drove to Regent's Park and left it outside the house where Setty lived.

Hume's wife went out to a hospital on the following morning, and he had to work against the clock. He already had a scheme for disposing of the body but it needed careful timing and more than a little luck to succeed. He was not sure how long his wife would be away. First, he went round the corner, bought a hacksaw and waited while an old carving knife was sharpened for him. 'Be quick,' Hume laughingly told the man who did it, 'the joint is on the table!'

Hume calculated that he had ninety minutes to strip the corpse and reduce it to manageable proportions before the daily woman, Mrs Stride, arrived. He had no knowledge of anatomy and sawing up bones is not only hard but very noisy work. However, to his surprise, the job was not too messy. Hume did not actually describe how he carried out the dismembering operation. He remarked casually later that he thought that what he was doing was not hurting Setty but was saving his own life. He made the body up into three parcels, each of which he wrapped in felt. The torso went back into the cupboard and he took the two other parcels, one containing the head and the other the legs, downstairs – Hume's flat was on the first floor – and put them in his car. The money Hume extracted from Setty's wallet, amounting to a large sum of new £5 notes with consecutive serial numbers, went into Hume's pocket. This was a mistake, although the motive for Setty's murder was almost certainly money. The notes had been paid to Setty by a man who had bought a Wolseley car from him and when Hume began to spend them the police were able to track him down. Greatly to Hume's annoyance, more than a thousand pounds' worth of notes were stained with Setty's blood and he had to burn them – so he said.

For a man with three parcels of a chopped-up body to dispose of, Hume behaved with notable coolness. He had failed to qualify as an R.A.F. pilot because of his inability to navigate, but a few years before he had joined the United Services Flying Club at Elstree as a civilian, and had acquired a 'C' licence to fly, which gave him access to the club's two-seater Auster aircraft. There was a small snag when he arrived at the airfield and asked the flight office if he could hire an aircraft; he had not paid for the previous aircraft he had hired. But he peeled off ten £5 notes from Setty's roll and he was in credit again.

Hume flew from Elstree towards Southend with the two parcels of Setty's remains in the passenger seat. He headed southwards for the French coast and, skirting the Channel Islands, flew on until he could see quite clearly the houses and farm buildings of France. But before he disposed of the parcels, he had other incriminating evidence to get rid of – the dagger with which he had killed Setty and the hacksaw and knife he had used to cut up the body. He threw the implements out of the aircraft first, and afterwards, when the two parcels went through the aircraft door, Hume noted that they must have sunk like stones. He saw them hit the water and when he looked again they had disappeared. Hume had left Elstree at 4.30 p.m. but the operation had taken longer than he expected. Because of the lateness of the hour, he changed his plans when he landed at Southend Airport. He parked the aircraft and hired a car to take him back to London. But even Hume had a conscience. When he got home, he remembered that he had left his Alsatian dog locked in his car at Elstree. He immediately telephoned the duty officer and arranged for the dog to be looked after.

Hume has not put on record how he slept on the night of 4 October. He has described his state of turmoil when he was in the witness box at the Old Bailey, telling a story that he hoped would clear him. In the small hours, if he was not asleep, he may have thought of the success of his plans so far. The murder weapons had gone for ever. The parcels containing the legs and head would never be seen again, with luck. But in the coal cupboard there still remained the grisly evidence of the torso to be disposed of. Would his luck still hold when he came to do that?

He believed correctly that there were no finger-prints at the flat to betray him and he had arranged for the sitting-room carpet to be cleaned as a precaution, in case it was stained. If Hume slept peacefully that night, he cannot have awakened with a very easy mind. He had called in a painter to re-stain the surrounds of the sitting room to get rid of possible bloodstains. When asked to explain why re-staining should be necessary, he said airily that he had it done two or three times every year – though presumably not always because there were marks of blood to remove. The man who did the staining was useful when Hume began to move the torso from the flat down to the car. 'This is heavy, Guv,' said the sweating painter. 'What have you got in it?' 'Fish,' said Hume facetiously.

The disposal of Setty's torso caused no special problems, though Hume had one or two nasty moments when he was airborne. Hume thought the easiest way to get the package out of the aircraft would be to prop it against the unlocked door, go into a dive and hope that the body would fall free as he pulled out. Hume had unfortunately forgotten that the torso had lain in the coal cupboard overnight and inevitably some of the coal dust had clung to it. The door of the aircraft did fly open as he planned but the uprush of air stirred the dust into a little storm inside the aircraft. Half-blinded Hume struggled to regain control of the aircraft as it plunged towards the sea. At the last moment, he managed to pull out of the dive. When he had straightened out and gained height the torso had gone but, to Hume's horror, he saw it floating on the surface without its felt wrapping. For a wild moment, he thought he would ditch the aircraft near the body, make sure the corpse went under and then swim back to the shore. He quickly changed his mind. His navigation had let him down, as often before. He saw that he was much nearer the shore than he had aimed to be. He was in a panic. His one aim now was to get away from the spot and the incriminating bundle. But he was lost and had no idea how to get to Southend, let alone Elstree. Finally, he decided to take a chance with a crash landing and brought the Auster down in a field of cabbages near Gravesend.

Seventeen days were to elapse before an Essex farm labourer came across the misused torso. Hume said that he tried to carry on normally while waiting for the news that it had been washed ashore. Setty, of course, had been reported missing and the police questioned many of his cronies in Warren Street and the drinking clubs he frequented. But Hume had conducted all his deals with Setty in a furtive way and no one suspected that there was any connection between the two men. Once the torso was found, however, it was soon identified. Hume had chopped off the head and legs but for some reason not the arms. At New Scotland Yard, the top finger-print expert, Detective-Chief Superintendent Fred Cherrill, was itching to try out a new technique for taking finger-prints from bodies that had been in the water a long time. The technique consisted of removing sections from fingers, treating them with a special solution, putting the sections on the tips of rubber gloves he was wearing, and finger-printing them. All this naturally would have been a waste of time if Setty had led a blameless life. But he had been in trouble twenty years before and his prints in the Yard's records matched those taken from the torso. As soon as the £5 notes Hume had stolen from Setty began to circulate, the police stepped up the search for the unknown thief and murderer.

Dr Camps had provided the police with their first clue when he said that the body had been dropped from a height. The Yard detective chiefs, Colin MacDougal and John Jamieson, treating the case as one of undoubted murder, reasoned that the torso might have fallen from a cliff, but could have been dropped from an aircraft. All the local airports in Essex and the neighbouring counties were visited and at Elstree an aircraft fitter named William Davy remembered that on 5 October, Hume had hired an Auster and had flown off with two parcels he had brought with him. The aircraft was traced to Southend and the staff there told the police that there were no parcels in it when Hume arrived. Hume was in bed when the detectives went to arrest him and from that moment, said Hume, he concocted a story which was almost as fantastic as the crime he had committed. 'Lies rolled off my tongue,' he boasted.

In retrospect, it seems incredible that the jury believed the cock-and-bull story Hume first told when he was taken to Albany Street Police Station. He said at first that he knew no one named Setty but agreed that he had hired an aircraft on 5 and 6 October at Elstree and had thrown three parcels into the sea when he was flying at about one thousand feet. Hume laughed at the idea that the parcels contained parts of a body and said the contents were parts of a printing press which had been used for forging stamps and coupons for rationed goods. Three men called 'Mac', 'Green', and 'The Boy' had brought the parcels to his flat when his wife was out. He did not know where they lived and the descriptions he gave of the men were in such general terms that the police were sure they did not exist. Hume said they could be found dealing in cars on the Warren Street kerbside but although detectives

46

haunted the area for days they could find neither the men nor anyone who knew them.

'The Boy', said Hume, offered him £50 to dump the first two parcels they had brought in the sea. When 'The Boy' produced a revolver to speed up the deal, Hume felt he had no alternative but to agree. His mission accomplished, he returned to the flat and found the three men there again. This time, the spokesman was 'Mac', who said they were going to give Hume a chance to earn another £50 by dumping a third parcel in the sea. Hume agreed to do it next day, but as he was taking the heavy parcel downstairs to the car he realized that all was not as it should be. Whatever was in the parcel made a gurgling sound and, said Hume, 'it crossed my mind that it might be Setty's body, as I had read in the newspapers that he was missing'. The police thought this statement was rather startling, and even more startling was the fact that Hume did nothing about it.

The medical evidence in this sensational case was not particularly sensational, but Camps and Teare between them gave a number of interesting facts about the human body. Camps' finding at the post mortem was that the cause of death was shock and haemorrhage due to multiple frontal stab wounds and that death would have come rapidly, within a matter of minutes. Camps did not believe in histrionics in the witness box, but when he was asked how quickly the five wounds could have been inflicted he gave a demonstration. It took between three and four seconds. Camps said the wounds were probably inflicted forty-eight hours before the body was put in the sea but that time 'must be purely speculative'.

'Can you think,' asked Mr Humphreys, 'of any way in which the parcel of that man's trunk, bound up by felt, could have made the stains that were found in the flat in different places?' Camps could not. The inference was that the bloodstains had been caused while Setty was fighting for his life, and, since he was a powerful man, someone must have held Setty from behind while the stabbing took place. 'Do you think,' Mr R. F. Levy, Q.C., prosecuting, asked Dr Teare, 'that Setty was killed by one single assailant?' Teare took so long to reply that the judge asked him whether he was considering if it was a medical question. After about two minutes, Teare replied, 'I think the absence of marks of defence on the body

47

renders it more likely that he was killed by more than one person.' The answer posed an awkward question because, if Setty had been killed by more than one person, why was Hume alone standing in the dock?

Dr Teare explained that when a person died suddenly or violently the blood lost its power to clot. Generally speaking, this took ninety minutes and then the blood remained fluid. It would dry like any other fluid but it would not coagulate.

Mr Levy asked about the quantity of blood in Setty's body at the time of the stabbing and Teare agreed with the evidence Camps had already given that it would vary between fairly wide limits but he would expect it to have had approximately thirteen pints of blood. And if the head and legs were detached from the body, how much would remain in the torso? 'I should say approximately between eight and ten pints,' said Teare. This was also Camps' estimate.

Teare gave what to laymen was a surprising answer, that in all probability not a great deal of blood would have escaped from the wounds. He would not necessarily expect spurting of blood from the wounds but rather a seeping of blood.

'Would there be a loss of very much blood in that way?' Teare was asked. 'I would not expect more than would soak the clothing of the breast. From the type of wound that Dr Camps has described, I should expect that there would be a considerable amount of coughing up of blood ... It would come out as a very violent cough.'

Teare differed from Camps' view that it was conceivable that the whole attack might have passed off very quietly, without struggle or noise of any kind. 'I would expect,' said Teare, 'either considerable resistance on the part of the attacked man, resulting, in all probability, in injuries to his body in the way of defence or protective injuries to hand or arm; or I should expect a volume of blood to be coughed up, which would be distributed over the assailant and adjacent structures, such as the walls or furniture and the floors.'

Although the pathologist declined to commit himself on whether Setty *had* remained silent during the attack, he differed also from Camps' view that there would be bruise marks on Setty's body where he had been restrained. 'A man could be restrained from

48

behind without any bruise marks developing,' he said.

'Suppose ... the torso were dropped in the way Hume said he dropped this one, what result would you expect from that?' he was asked. Dr Teare's reply was that he would expect that the impact would squeeze blood out of the folds in almost every direction.

The evidence for the prosecution, as Mr Humphreys said at the start of the trial, was entirely circumstantial – the strongest sort of evidence, as the late Lord Chief Justice Hewart was fond of pointing out – and Mr Justice Sellers, without the benefit of the hindsight of Hume's confession many years later, plainly thought that his story was too tall to be believed. The vital date in the case was 4 October, when Setty was believed to have been killed, and yet, asked the judge, 'what evidence have we after this trial, on the movements of Hume on that vital day? The fourth of October is, as far as the evidence relating to Hume is concerned, practically a blank and you may ask yourselves why it is.' Hume had asked the jury to accept – 'of course, improbable stories do happen', the judge interjected, caustically – that in broad daylight, somewhere between 2 p.m. and 3 p.m., three men had brought two parcels to his flat. 'You may think and there is no point in this unless you do think, which I do, that these two parcels were the remains of the dead man, Setty.' The judge favoured the theory of an attack by a gang, which included Hume. 'Do you think that this attack could have been made by Hume in the front without any sign which might be regarded as defence wounds to his hands or arms?'

The end of the trial was almost as confused as some of the evidence had been. The jury could not agree on a verdict. A fresh jury was sworn but the prosecution offered no evidence and Hume was found not guilty of murder. The second indictment charging Hume with being an accessory to murder by disposing of the body was heard and, after a brief adjournment, Hume pleaded guilty. His sentence was twelve years' imprisonment.

Prison, however, did not subdue Hume's murderous instincts. He said later that the only thing he regretted when he came out of prison was that his dog had been 'put down'. He changed his name to Donald Brown, went to Switzerland, and, in successive raids, shot two British bank guards in robbery attempts. After his third murder, a taxi-driver, he was caught, and the sentence of the Zurich court was life imprisonment. In prison, Hume was uncontrollable and he is still held at Regensdorf Jail in solitary confinement. He has a picture of himself on the wall of his tiny cell and reads and re-reads newspaper stories about himself. He keeps fit by doing exercises in his cell. Father Pereira, a Catholic priest who is prison chaplain, thinks he is a psychopath. 'I am convinced,' he says, 'that he is of little use to humanity, and perhaps never will be.' But Mr Hugh Gilmartin, former British consul at Zurich, who has been an official visitor and has endured his constant insults and rages, has reported a change in Hume's behaviour. He has become outwardly pleasant and friendly to the prison staff, who believe that the change is due to the fact that Hume could be eligible for parole soon. The Swiss would like to see the back of Hume but would be reluctant to let loose a violent murderer who might kill yet again, even in his native land.

A Faked Suicide

Francis Camps, later forensic consultant to the British army, was vitally involved in an army trial in which the murderer was convicted by the pathological evidence more than two years after the murder had occurred. It was a case in which a young army pathologist, a Captain Womack, drew a wrong conclusion after he had conducted a two-day post mortem, and Camps, who said it was a mistake that anybody could have made, was able to put the record straight.

In his book *Practical Forensic Medicine* (written with Sir Bentley Purchase), Camps said that the type of violence used by Frederick 'Mick' Emmett-Dunne, a R.E.M.E. sergeant stationed at Duisburg in Germany in 1953, to kill another sergeant, Reginald 'Tich' Watters, had not been described in forensic literature before. He said it had never been used previously. It was the type resulting from a blow with the edge of the hand or wrist, used as a method of defence in ju-jitsu, or as a method of killing in unarmed combat. The methods of delivering the two sorts of blow are different and in both cases might be aimed deliberately at the larynx. Without harsh force, such blows might merely stun, although death from shock could result; but with severe force the thyroid cartilage which covers the adam's apple might be fractured and cause death, not usually instantaneously but certainly shortly afterwards.

Camps went into the subject with great thoroughness because, as so often happened in his specialist field, a man's life, in this case Emmett-Dunne's, depended on his experience and opinions. The injuries to the neck caused by a karate-type blow and those caused by hanging might not differ much to the comparatively inexperienced eye, but to a pathologist of Camps' standing they were obvious and crucial.

The crime occurred when the British Army of Occupation in Germany had been in full and settled swing for a number of years. Life in the British zone was pleasant and easy for the soldiers. The civilian population was friendly, and fraternization took place on a considerable scale. There was much inter-marriage between the army bachelors and German girls, and one of the soldiers who had acquired a German wife was 'Tich' Watters, a five foot nothing Yorkshire sergeant, who was on the staff of the R.E.M.E. Technical Training College in Duisburg.

Emmett-Dunne and Watters were apparently friends, but two men could not have been more different in appearance and character. Watters, with his easy-going ways, was both the butt and, at the same time, the life and soul of any party. He was the best type of N.C.O. in the peace-time British army, always approachable and cheerful, even with a hangover, which he usually had. Emmett-Dunne was tall, good-looking, conceited and almost the stage Irishman. He had previously served with the Royal Marines and had been through the North African campaign with the Irish Guards. He was taken prisoner and while 'in the bag' a brutal German guard had struck him in the back with a rifle and caused a permanent injury. Among other mishaps during his army career was a shooting incident at Blandford, when he had accidentally received bursts of Bren gun fire in both legs. He claimed that he had always liked army life, but those who served under him were known to be markedly less enthusiastic. He was not popular. He was also believed to be a thief. A matter of misused regimental funds was being enquired into by the army police and Emmett-Dunne was under open arrest pending a court-martial. 'I felt ostracized,' he said, when describing that period of his life at his court-martial for murder. 'Watters was one of the very few men who continued to treat me as a normal person and not a criminal.'

But Watters by this time certainly did not consider Emmett-Dunne as either a friend or a normal person. He had become jealous of the way his wife, Mia, and his colleague seemed to be getting on so well. Perhaps with good reason, if what the other army wives were saying was true. Vague hints were dropped after the drinks had been flowing at sergeants' mess social gatherings that Mia Watters and Emmett-Dunne were seeing each other often outside the normal social rounds. Occasionally, Watters confided his fears to close friends, one of whom was Q.M.S. Fred Cracknell. Watters said he thought some fishy business was going on between Emmett-Dunne and his wife. Only a month before he died, Watters seemed upset and told him he thought it funny that Emmett-Dunne should call at his flat every Sunday afternoon with newspapers. 'But,' said Q.M.S. Cracknell, 'I thought it had become an obsession with Sergeant Watters. He was of a jealous nature as far as his wife was concerned.'

Emmett-Dunne later admitted that he danced frequently with Mrs Watters but said it was only because she was a good dancer. 'I was very fond of her, possibly too much,' said Emmett-Dunne nonchalantly, 'but I flirted with everybody.' He denied telling a girl he took out that he was in love with a married woman. As for the evidence that he frequently drove past Watters' married quarters, and Mrs Watters often followed shortly afterwards in her own car, it was untrue. So was the story that he had been seen driving along an autobahn with Mrs Watters as a passenger.

The manner in which 'Tich' Watters was killed was disputed but there was no doubt he had died late on the night of 30 November or in the early hours of the following morning. Watters was trying to sell a car and had left his quarters to meet a potential buyer soon after seven o'clock. Emmett-Dunne himself had left the camp at 7.5 p.m. but was back by at least 7.25 p.m. Earlier in the evening Q.M.S. Charles Fry had spoken to Mrs Watters as she was playing cards in the mess bar and was to speak to her later, when she telephoned to say that her husband had not returned home. He organized a search and Emmett-Dunne told him that he had dropped

Watters outside the gates of Glamorgan Barracks earlier in the evening. It was not long before Emmett-Dunne and Armament Q.M.S. Fry found the body, with tongue protruding, hanging from the banisters of the entrance to block No. 3 of the barracks. A bucket, on which Watters had apparently stood, was on its side nearby. Fry went to telephone for help and when he returned found Emmett-Dunne trying to be sick against the wall. Fry asked him what had happened. 'As I took the body down, it gurgled and it made me feel sick,' he said. Fry said he thought the suicide had affected Emmett-Dunne's health because, when he saw him ten days later, he commented on the fact that Emmett-Dunne seemed to have lost a lot of weight. 'I reckon I have lost two stone,' Emmett-Dunne said.

The death of the little sergeant caused a great sensation in Duisburg army circles since it was completely unexpected. If he had taken his wife's supposed partiality for Emmett-Dunne at all seriously, he had not shown it outwardly. Emmett-Dunne, ever ready with mysterious remarks, had been heard to say that if somebody's wife didn't behave herself her husband would probably kill himself, but no one paid any attention to him.

However, if Emmett-Dunne's melodramatic story of the last minutes in the life of 'Tich' Watters was worth believing, Watters had been harbouring resentment against him and it came to the surface when the two men met at entrance No. 3 at the barracks after leaving the transport office. At first, said Emmett-Dunne, Watters had his back to him and appeared to be fumbling with something – 'a rope', exclaimed Emmett-Dunne loudly, when he gave evidence at his court-martial in Steel House, Dusseldorf. Emmett-Dunne often spoke during his time in the witness box of the 'impressions' he had, and this particular 'impression' was that Watters had just tied the end of the rope to the banisters.

He asked 'Tich' what he was doing and the subject of his friendship with Mrs Watters was brought up. 'Let's not have trivial differences and arguments,' he said. 'I have enough on my plate with my court-martial, without people like you turning against me.' The conversation was a continuation of unfriendly talk that had begun a few minutes before, when Watters said he was fed up playing second fiddle. He now accused Emmett-Dunne of having lived with his wife in the American zone, while he, Watters, was away on a big ten day military exercise called Grand Republic in the previous September. Emmett-Dunne told the little sergeant that he was talking nonsense but Watters would not accept this answer. 'You know what I am bloody-well talking about,' was the forthright army-style reply, 'I have got proof.'

Emmett-Dunne continued to deny that Mia and he were more than good friends, and said he was not such a fool as to break up his friendship with Watters. But Watters remained so angry that he seemed to Emmett-Dunne to be mad. 'You think you can run the barracks as you like,' Watters had said. 'You just take anything you want but I will put a stop to this.'

By this time, Watters had seated himself in the passenger seat of the car and Emmett-Dunne said he was standing outside the car, arguing and imploring Watters not to believe the stories he had been hearing. Suddenly, Watters produced a gun. 'It was looking right between my eyes,' he told the court, without batting an eyelid, 'I could see three or four rounds in it. I gained the impression that the cylinder of the pistol was about to turn, or,' as though this was a little nearer the truth, 'was actually moving.' This story was too incredible for Mr Mervyn Griffith-Jones to believe. 'Are you telling the court that in the dark with nothing except a little lamp in the roof, you were able to see that there was a round in the chamber of the revolver which was next to be fired?' he asked. Emmett-Dunne said he was.

The court waited again as if wondering how far Emmett-Dunne would now go. He said his hand was in the region of the car's light switch and that to avoid being shot he intended to stun his friend. 'I gained the impression' – the same pat phrase – 'that he was moving. As well as striking him, I threw myself on him to get the pistol. I got it and flicked it into the back of the car.' While Emmett-Dunne was talking, he crouched down in the witness box to give a demonstration of how this extraordinary scene had taken place.

Pausing a moment after his exertion, Emmett-Dunne said his next act was to go to the other side of the car, put his arms round Watters to get him out of the car, and support him to the barracks entrance steps. 'I thought he was coming round or going to speak or that he

54

had made a noise. I talked to him, although I don't truthfully know what I said. I got him past the first door but he had passed out.' Emmett-Dunne said he tripped over a piece of rope as he supported Watters along the wall. His inflection suddenly became quieter and sad. 'I slapped his face and got no response,' he said. 'I saw bubbles of saliva on his mouth and took his pulse. There was no response and I realized he was dead.'

Despite the fact that Watters was dead, Emmett-Dunne said his first thought was to get help from the M.I. (Medical Inspection) room but it was shut. 'When I turned away I was frightened,' he said, 'I didn't know what to do but I knew I had killed a man.'

Emmett-Dunne had a half-brother, Ronald Emmett, who was in the same unit. Emmett-Dunne professed to be more fond of Ronald than of anybody else but later Ronald made it clear that the feelings were not reciprocated. Emmett-Dunne said that when he knew that Watters was dead, he did not want his 'brother', as he always called Ronald, to know what had happened. In the next breath, however, he was telling the court that he had immediately sent a soldier to find Ronald in order to tell him. Emmett-Dunne claimed that he was 'shaking like a leaf' when his brother arrived. The conversation seems to have been confused but it finally emerged that he had told Ronald that he had had an argument with a chap and that he was dead.

Mr Derek Curtis-Bennett, who defended Emmett-Dunne, knew that the court would wish to be informed, truthfully if possible, whose idea it had been to make Watters' death look like suicide. Emmett-Dunne fenced. 'My brother said something and I said: "Oh, what shall I do?" He said: "Look! Did you have an argument with him? Did you strike him?" I said: "Yes. I got him as far as here."' Court reporters then timed a pause as long as twenty seconds before Emmett-Dunne went on with his story: 'I cannot truthfully say whether my brother or I asked if there was anything we could do. While walking about the well of the staircase, I realized the rope was there. I cannot truthfully say other than that it was a simultaneous agreement that we should move the body to make it look like suicide. Afterwards I swore ... I would never give him away.'

If Emmett-Dunne could not 'say truthfully' who had suggested that Watters' 'suicide' should be faked, Ronald Emmett most certainly could. On the day of Watters' death, he had not been feeling very well and was lying down after tea when he received a message that Emmett-Dunne wanted to see him. He said his half-brother was standing by his car in the car park and told him to get inside, giving him a caution to remember that he was his brother. Emmett-Dunne then said he had killed a man after an argument. 'I struck him or pushed him and he fell. I found he was dead.' He pointed to Watters' body, lying under a gas cape, with his knees drawn up to his face. Emmett-Dunne said he wanted to make it look like suicide, and for this purpose the body must be put by the stairs. While they were talking, he heard people coming down the stairs and ran out to hide in the bushes. When he went back he noticed the rope for the first time. One end was round the banister and the other round the dead man's neck. 'We both lifted him up,' said Emmett. 'I held him up while my brother fastened the other end of the rope to the banister.' The bucket was so placed that it looked as if the dead man had kicked it away in the process of hanging himself. 'Was the idea of hanging the body a mutual idea?' Ronald was asked by Mr Curtis-Bennett. The answer was an uncompromising 'No'. The rope, incidentally, was never found.

Thirty-six hours after Watters was found hanging, Dr Alan Womack, a junior pathologist attached to the British army in Germany, carried out a post mortem. It was an extremely thorough examination but Dr Womack candidly admitted his inexperience and said that he had never before dealt with a case of death by hanging. He found the thyroid cartilage was fractured. There was bruising of the larynx and wind-pipe consistent with the cartilage being knocked back against the larynx, which it had penetrated. The muscles of the throat were also bruised. Dr Womack formed the view, after studying the battered and discoloured neck and throat, that the furrow from the rope was higher than the bruising of the muscles of the throat. He found no other injuries, but half an hour to an hour before his death Watters had had a meal, which seemed somewhat unusual for a man in the frame of mind to commit suicide. Dr Womack said there was another little bone in the throat just below the thyroid cartilage (the cricoid bone) and his impression was that this bone was also fractured. But the young doctor said that he had not opened up the tissues but had formed his view after feeling it with his fingers. The medical evidence seemed straightforward and, though there were puzzling features about the case, the army court had felt justified in returning a verdict of suicide by hanging.

It was common knowledge in army circles that neither army personnel nor German civilians employed at the barracks believed that Watters had killed himself. But at the time the investigations were going on and the rumours were buzzing noisily, Lieutenant Colonel Frank Elliott, the assistant provost marshal of the Special Investigation Department, was on leave. As soon as he returned he decided that further investigations into the affair were desirable and the commissioner of the Metropolitan Police loaned him Detective-Superintendent Colin MacDougal for the purpose.

The two men and their assistants were thoroughly experienced detectives. One of their first calls on receiving the assignment was the London headquarters of the Judo Club, to observe experiments. Two pieces of wood, an inch long, across and deep, were placed between the arms of chairs, and an expert, delivering a moderate blow with the side of his hand, was able to split them easily. If the wood had been a larynx and the object of the blow had been merely to stun, the blow would have gone far beyond its purpose.

More experiments were carried out at the military hospital at Hostert in Germany, and were aimed chiefly at finding out how vertical fractures of the thyroid cartilage could be caused. Larynxes of different ages were given blows of varying strengths and in a high proportion of those hit in this way there was discernible damage. Those who were to prosecute later had done their homework thoroughly.

Emmett-Dunne had hoodwinked the army authorities and his army career resumed its normal course. His next posting, six months later, to Catterick in North Yorkshire, could not, on the face of it, have been engineered by Emmett-Dunne but experienced and wily N.C.O.s have been known to find ways of manipulating army procedures, when it is to their benefit to do so. Emmett-Dunne said he had heard at Catterick that Leeds was the centre of the tailoring business – it was, but of wholesale tailoring, not retail – and so went there on a day off to buy a suit. Only a believer in fairy stories would have credited the coincidences that followed. After ordering his suit, he dropped into a small pub called the Ingram Arms Hotel for a drink. He found, to his astonishment needless to say, that it was run by a married sister of Sergeant Watters. To his even greater astonishment, Mia Watters was visiting her sister-in-law at that very moment. The two old friends talked for a time but no arrangement was made to meet again. But fate seemed to have ordained that they should meet again, and two or three weeks later, when Emmett-Dunne was in Leeds again, he spotted Mia in a cinema queue.

Emmett-Dunne denied that at this time he was in love with Mia, but said there had been talk of marriage after that meeting. Emmett-Dunne thought she might be happier in Germany and had offered her money for the fare but she said her life was her own, and she intended to get a job at the Naafi. As Emmett-Dunne remembered the conversation, he had said: 'If you are looking for a home and security, I will marry you.' She said 'No. You are a bigger drunkard than my husband.' Emmett-Dunne repeated on oath at his trial that he was not in love with her, but eventually they did marry – a marriage of convenience, it seemed. 'I agreed because my actions had lost her her livelihood,' said Emmett-Dunne. 'We were to marry on the understanding that I should live my own life but provide a home.' But the inference that it had been a platonic arrangement was disproved when the new Mrs Emmett-Dunne later said there had been no sexual intercourse between them – until after marriage.

Medical evidence was crucial at Emmett-Dunne's trial but the real starting point was the gossip caused by the wedding. In Duisburg the eyebrows of the army wives had no sooner been raised by the news than their tongues began to chatter.

But what could have been idle gossip – 'tongue-wagging' as Mr Curtis-Bennett called it – might have been ignored if the man who knew most of the facts had not decided to speak to the police. Ronald Emmett, back in civilian life, was living in Kirby, Cheshire. He had read of his half-brother's marriage to the dead man's widow but, although he was more suspicious than he had been, he put aside the thought that there was anything unusual about it. The tragedy must have drawn the two people together, and at the time of Watters' death he had had Emmett-Dunne's assurance that it had been an accident. If he had not believed it, he would certainly not have helped to fake Watters' suicide.

The news that Watters' body had been exhumed made him think again. He knew that the army inquest on Watters had reached the wrong conclusion and thought that if he were to give the correct version it would be helpful. His statement was taken by the civilian police at Hoylake, who passed it to the army, and the consequence was that Emmett-Dunne was arrested and that Ronald Emmett stood in the witness box to give evidence against him.

Mr Curtis-Bennett, in cross-examination, immediately asked the pertinent question after Emmett had said that 'this thing' had got on his nerves and that was why he went to the police. 'Was it not because you were frightened you might be involved that you went to the police?' he asked. 'No,' said Emmett. 'Up to the moment I read about the marriage I believed it was an accident. When I read about the marriage I began to think it might not have been an accident.'

The arrest of Emmett-Dunne took place in Taunton, Somerset, where he was living with Mia. For a man who protested his innocence so much, he made most strenuous efforts to avoid trial when he appeared at Bow Street, London, charged with murder. He said he had been born in Dublin. Although his life had been spent in the British army, he immediately claimed that as an Irish citizen he could not be tried by a British court for a crime committed on foreign soil. This was correct in law, but if Emmett-Dunne thought this would be the end of the matter he was disappointed. The military police took over before Emmett-Dunne tasted freedom, flew him to the military corrective establishment at Bielefeld, former headquarters of an S.S. Panzer group of the German army, and charged him with murder. Brigadier D. L. Betts and seven more officers formed the court-martial, with Mr Charles Cahn of the Judge-Advocate-General's department to give guidance on law.

Camps was flown to Cologne Military Cemetery to supervise the exhumation of the body of Watters, and when identity had been established by means of a signet ring he carried out a second post mortem. He found the larynx was loose and removed it. Photographs were taken before the larynx was sent to London. The most dramatic thing Camps did when he gave evidence on the fifth day of Emmett-Dunne's trial was to produce it in a transparent box.

While everyone else in court gazed with riveted attention at the exhibit, Emmett-Dunne put his hands up to his eyes until it had been taken away. Camps, with his usual thoroughness, produced diagrams of the structure of the neck, so that the court could follow his evidence more easily. The only way in which his findings differed from those of his younger colleague was that the cricoid bone was not broken, as Dr Womack had thought. The wrong finding would inevitably lead to the wrong conclusion, as Mr Griffith-Jones brought out in his examination of Camps.

'In your view,' asked Griffith-Jones, 'could this man have died from hanging?' The answer was 'No'. The next question was: 'What did he die from?' 'In my view,' said Camps, 'he died from shock from a blow on the neck.' 'Death could be caused by a very light blow?' 'Oh yes, indeed.' And the last question: 'Would it be possible for a man to die by a blow on the neck, although the blow did not cause a fracture of the thyroid cartilage?' The answer was 'Yes'.

There is no doubt that Emmett-Dunne knew exactly how to kill a man with the edge of his hand in a chopping blow from the elbow. An Irish Guards instructor, Sergeant Robert Chalmers, asked by Mr Curtis-Bennett whether a man the height of Emmett-Dunne, slightly facing another man sitting in the position of Watters, could stun him with a blow, replied wryly, 'That is the general idea.' But he disagreed with the suggestion that if a man in Watters' position pointed a revolver at another man where Emmett-Dunne was standing the way to deal with the situation would be to use a hand-chop. 'It is one of the last things I would do,' said the instructor. 'I would slap the weapon away, grab at the hand and break a finger.'

The prosecution, said Mr Griffith-Jones, had given the court a jigsaw of facts, all fitting into one picture; even if Emmett-Dunne had kept strict control over his emotions, he would have found it difficult to make his thin, often absurd story sound plausible. It was riddled with inconsistencies and patent lies. The manner in which he told it made matters worse for himself. He gave his evidence in an arrogant parade ground voice and was rude when the opportunity occurred, and even without it. 'It is a pity,' said Mr Griffith-Jones at one stage, 'that you don't answer the question put, instead of looking ahead to see what it is leading to.' 'If you would put the question to me straight, I would answer it straight,' retorted Emmett-Dunne. The fact that for four and a half hours he was under questioning by one of the most deadly cross-examiners of his day, and losing all the time, must have unnerved even a man who had a high opinion of his own intelligence. Those concerned with the trial might have been forgiven for thinking that Emmett-Dunne was behaving so outrageously that he was insane – or wanted people to think so. But the judge, knowing that the prisoner was on trial for his life, hardly interfered at all. It was simpler, it seemed, to let Emmett-Dunne convict himself by his own words and actions.

Camps was called in towards the end of the trial to give the *coup de grâce*. Emmett-Dunne made it known that he was anxious to demonstrate exactly how he had struck the fatal blow and the members of the court, together with counsel, went into the courtyard to watch. A private soldier took the place of Watters and seated himself in a car. Emmett-Dunne bent down and swung his arm in the same way as he said he had done when he killed Watters. Camps had a quick word with Mr Griffith-Jones and went straight into the witness box. He said the injuries caused by a blow such as Emmett-Dunne had demonstrated would be to the *side* of the neck. 'The injuries I found must have been inflicted by a central blow – quite definitely,' said Camps.

The pathologist's special knowledge had floored Emmett-Dunne and Mr Curtis-Bennett could not help him. 'I quite understand your theory,' he began. Camps interrupted him. 'This is not a theory,' he said firmly. 'This is straightforward mechanics.'

Emmett-Dunne was sentenced to death by hanging and did not appeal. He petitioned the Queen for mercy and was turned down. But he did not hang because capital punishment had been abolished in Germany and he was given instead a sentence of life imprisonment. While he was still in prison he was granted a decree *nisi* in the London Divorce Court in 1964 on the ground of adultery by his wife. Mrs Emmett-Dunne had changed her name to Drake by this time and did not contest a charge that she had committed adultery in Gloucester Place Mews, St Marylebone.

Christie: Mass Murderer of Notting Hill

The most important case in which Camps as a pathologist helped to convict a murderer was undoubtedly that of 'Reg' Christie, 'the Monster of Rillington Place', who, in the picturesque words of one writer on the case, 'made of his Notting Hill flat a graveyard of ravished whores'.

It was really two cases in one and was straightforward and baffling at the same time. It raised most of the questions, except greed and money, that arise in murders that seem to be unnecessary and pointless: motive, sanity, sex, miscarriage of justice and vanity. It seems unlikely that John Reginald Halliday Christie ever considered that his name would go down in criminal history as the one mass murderer that every generation is supposed to throw up. He was too outwardly respectable and thought himself a cut above his fellow clerks and citizens of the same type. The impulse to murder must have been latent all his life but he was forty-three years old before he gave way to it.

Camps gave his opinion that mass murderers do not 'burn out'. Once they start, they must go on and on. If this is so, Christie must be an exception to the rule, though only partially so. Christie murdered first in the August of 1943 and the second time fourteen months later. The appetite seemed satiated and for eight years the impulse was dormant. Then he proved Camps' theory correct by murdering four times in quick succession.

Hardly anybody who met Christie had a good word to say for him. He had a mean and crooked nature and was a liar before he began to tell the perhaps excusable lies in an attempt to save his neck. He could claim respectability in the thirties because nobody in the London district where he was then living knew that he had been a thief and could be violent even with women when crossed. He had seen the inside of prison several times – for false pretences, stealing postal orders when he was a temporary postman, and stealing money and goods, including a motor car. That a man of his character should have been enrolled as a War Reserve policeman can be accounted for only by the fact that he concealed his record or was not asked about it. Those who knew him at that period of his life said that he was officious and never unwilling to use his authority even in the most petty of cases.

His photographs show him to be an ordinary type of man – if such a type can be said to exist – of upright physique with glittering eyes but almost bald and not the sort of man to attract women. My old friend the late Colonel 'Pip' Youngman-Carter, the artist, who observed Christie in court and afterwards painted him, saw beyond that. He told me that Christie looked an evil man. In his studio when he was actually painting his portrait, the face that emerged was cold, unworried and foxy. 'Two days' association with it made me almost physically sick,' he wrote later. 'The woman cleaning my studio, who had no idea of the subject of the portrait, asked me to put it away because it was frightening.'

The boy, who was to grow up to look like another mass murderer, Adolf Eichmann, was from Yorkshire – born in the cold, windy, cobble street town of Halifax. His father was a dour, silent, worthy but unfriendly carpet maker, who, if he had any affection for his seven children, in the Yorkshire way never showed it. Reg Christie was an ordinary boy with ordinary, if a trifle wayward, habits, but he was physically unlike the sturdy, rough-hewn Yorkshire lads with whom he grew up. He was what is known in those parts as sickly, always out of sorts (possibly to attract the attention of his mother), and he was not much interested in games. He sang in the choir, and it is interesting to note that another Yorkshire mass murderer, John George 'Chink' Haigh, was also a chorister.

Early sex awakening is not, as is sometimes believed, confined to the warmer countries and by the time they were what is now known as teenagers the young men of Halifax took at least as much interest in girls as they did in sport.

Christie was no exception but the girl he picked – or it may have been the other way round – realized after some torrid petting that she was getting nowhere with him. She could not rouse him. 'You are no good to me,' she said petulantly as they parted. She told a friend, who told a friend, and word was soon passed on that Reg Christie was hopeless with girls. The quick-witted Yorkshire lads thought it shameful in a jokey way and Christie became known as 'Reggie-no-prick' in the neighbourhood.

Christie was sixteen when the Great War broke out and he enlisted in the local regiment, the Duke of Wellington's, as soon as he was old enough. He was gassed in the 1918 German 'push', and while undoubtedly he suffered injuries to his eyes and voice, so that for a time he could not see or speak, he seems to have made the most of them. His sight returned after five months but, though the army specialists could find nothing wrong with his voice-box, he continued to be speechless for more than three years. Some doctors thought he was malingering. If that were so, he suddenly seems to have decided that the sympathy he might attract because of his disability was outweighed by the inconvenience and his voice returned spontaneously.

In 1920 he married Ethel Waddington, a good-looking Yorkshire girl, and at his trial he said the marriage was happy, even though it broke up after only three years.

Christie's criminal record was mainly for minor offences. At his trial, he voluntarily gave evidence of his misdemeanours and the police admitted that they would never have been traced had he not confessed to them. Perhaps there was a reason. If he could show that he was merely a small-time rogue, the jury might be sympathetic towards him for finding himself on a capital charge – a monstrous charge, really involving not one but five women. We do not know the devious workings of Christie's mind about this and many other matters. We have a fair idea, however, of his many previous lapses into petty crime, and of his violence, including a 'murderous' attack with a cricket bat on a woman, his penury, his marital troubles, his phobias and lies, and the places where he lived.

London had been Christie's home for many years when war broke out. He joined the War Reserve Police and did his duty well during the blitz. His wife was in Sheffield and he was living alone at No. 10 Rillington Place. But his service in the force came to an abrupt end in 1943. The police authorities do not look kindly on 'affairs' with women, whether they involve regular or temporary policemen, and the police chiefs at Harrow Road had heard that Christie was spending too much time, too frequently, at a young woman's flat near No. 10 Rillington Place. Christie was sacked and the sequel to the affair, a few years later when the husband came home from the war, was that he gave Christie a thoroughly deserved good hiding. Not surprisingly, Christie, while pretending to give his evidence in the frankest way, did not mention this incident.

Camps was fully occupied at the time with what was known as the Setty or Torso case, which was headlined in all the newspapers. He could not know of Christie's lurid background, nor obviously of the more serious events destined to take place at Rillington Place later in the year. He was not professionally concerned with them though, as with anything in the human sphere, he was fascinated by the background as it unfolded in court. Yet he was involved. Camps' raw material in life was bodies and two living people were to become corpses in the dirty, ramshackle house in Rillington Place. Christie had turned from petty crime to murder.

Christie's first victim was a tall, good-looking Austrian girl, Ruth Margarete Christine Fuerst, whom he said he had met in a Bayswater snack bar while looking for a man wanted for stealing. Her skull, assembled under Camps' direction from 110 pieces, now stands in the laboratory of Professor R. J. Harrison of Cambridge, who supervised the work. Miss Fuerst had come from Vienna as a refugee in 1939 and subsequently made a living as best she could. Christie's second wife had gone to see her relatives in Sheffield and the flat was empty that night. Miss Fuerst went willingly to Rillington Place and, according to Christie, they made love. Whether the act was unsatisfactory and put in Christie's mind thoughts of strangulation for the first time we do not know. At his trial, Christie said she was 'inclined to be affectionate towards me. She wanted us to get together.' Certainly Miss Fuerst went back again; they made love but this time he strangled her.

It is perhaps understandable that his recollection of all that happened with Ruth Fuerst was somewhat vague. He murdered several more times after that before he was arrested and tried. But he must have remembered the panic he experienced when he prized open the floor boards in the front room, put in Miss Fuerst's body and clothes, and immediately afterwards received a telegram from his wife to say that she and her brother were arriving from Sheffield that evening. Christie had to sweat it out until the following afternoon when his wife went shopping and he was able to move the body to the comparative safety of the wash house. Later he carried it into the garden and put it in a hole he had dug.

There is no doubt that by this time Christie was seriously engrossed in the business of finding ways of causing death. He had invented a 'death jar' which was an ordinary square jar with two holes bored through the screw-top lid. The jar was filled with the old-fashioned, strong-smelling Friar's Balsam. He attached one end of a rubber tube to a gas jet and led the other end into the balsam. Another tube was pushed through the second hole in the lid and the other end given to the victim to hold near her face when the gas was turned on. Since the smell of the balsam smothered the smell of the gas, the victim would be completely unaware that she was being murdered. Camps called the apparatus cumbersome but agreed it was possible to murder with it, provided the victims were incurious. This problem Christie solved by draping a cover over the victim's head and eyes.

Christie was soon to prove that his apparatus was workable but only he knew for certain who his first victim was. Because of his prevarications, there is no way of knowing whether it was Ruth Fuerst or his second victim, Muriel Amelia Eady, a nurse at the Ultra Radio Company's works at Park Royal where Christie began working after his dismissal from the police.

Miss Eady had a boyfriend and Christie had a wife; and it was not long before Christie suggested a tea party at Rillington Place. Other small outings followed and soon Christie was professing concern about Nurse Eady's catarrhal sniffle and offering to cure it. He had impressed Miss Eady with talk of his medical knowledge acquired through the St John Ambulance Brigade and she agreed to let him try. Mrs Christie was away and they were alone. Watched eagerly by Christie, she inhaled the gas. Christie said he strangled her during the process, took her from the bedroom and put her into the wash house until the time was propitious for burying her in the garden.

Christie's defence at his trial was to be insanity and he must have thought that general haziness in answering questions and an apparent lack of appreciation of the dreadful things he had done would help the jury to think he was mad. From the start, his evidence was spattered with such phrases as 'I don't remember', 'I don't know', 'I am not sure', and 'I think so'. His reply 'I think so. I don't know' to counsel's question 'Is that the first person (Ruth Fuerst) you killed in your life?' tried the patience of Mr Derek Curtis-

Bennett, who defended him. 'You don't even know that!' he exclaimed.

Christie said he did not know whether he had killed anybody between 1944 and 1949 but agreed he may have done more killings than he was going to talk about. The date 1949 is of great importance in this case because it is the point at which the pathetic couple, Timothy and Beryl Evans, step on to the stage. Timothy Evans was to be branded a murderer and his case was to become important in the annals of criminology. It was to be debated at length in the House of Commons and in the press. After he was hanged, and more particularly after Christie himself was convicted, the furious debate continued between those who favoured capital punishment and those who believed there had been a miscarriage of justice and hanging should be abolished.

The contrast between Mr and Mrs Evans as a couple was remarkable, Evans, a short, ferret-faced, violent man of low mentality, was known to be a pathological liar; his wife was a sophisticated woman from a middle-class family. Those who knew them marvelled that they had ever met, let alone married. But it was not a happy marriage. Money was always short and, like the ill-favoured Christie, Evans was able to attract other women. Soon after the wedding, there was trouble about a friend of Beryl's, a blonde named Lucy. Evans went away with her for a couple of days, but he returned and was forgiven.

Timothy Evans, who was born on the same late September day in 1924 that Christie was sentenced to nine months' imprisonment for theft, fathered a child born in October 1948. The parents lived in the tiny top flat at 10 Rillington Place and twelve months later Mrs Evans, pregnant again, was depressed at living in such sordid conditions and talking of suicide.

The prosecution's case was that Evans lost his job and, as his own depression and poverty increased, strangled his wife in a violent temper and at the same time murdered his child. He was charged with the murder of his child only. He told various lies to account for the absence of his wife and baby, but the Christies gave evidence that on 8 November they had heard a thud over their heads in the middle of the night, and then some movement. Next morning, a rather wild-looking Evans told Christie a number of things : his wife had taken the child to Bristol or Brighton – it was never clear which; he had packed in his job; and he was selling his furniture. Of the three statements, the only true one was about the furniture. Evans then went to an aunt in Wales but, in the meantime, his mother had written to the aunt providing evidence that Evans was a liar. Evans, determined to sort things out if he could, went to the Welsh police and made four successive statements, in the second of which he said that Christie had murdered his wife and child.

At the two day trial of Evans, Christie was the principal witness and the suggestion was put to him that he was responsible for the deaths of the mother and child; or that, if it was not so, he knew much more about the deaths than he had said. 'That's a lie,' was Christie's retort. It was his word against that of Evans. 'I never done it, Mum, Christie done it,' Evans said to his mother after he had been charged.

The way in which Mrs Evans died will always be a mystery. While Christie and his wife claimed that they tried to stop Mrs Evans from taking pills to cause an abortion, Mrs Evans told her husband that she intended to have one and that Christie had promised to do the abortion himself. Evans said she did not tell him that, as Christie later said, she had offered to let him make love to her as the price. How Christie was to procure an abortion or whether he had the knowledge to do so was never mentioned. Later, Christie said the killing occurred at lunch-time when Beryl was intent on suicide. He used gas and strangled her but could not raise an erection to have intercourse.

Evans said Christie was waiting for him at the bottom of the stairs when he came home and told him that his wife was dead in the bedroom. 'It's bad news. It didn't work,' said Christie. It is assumed that Christie frightened Evans into helping him to take the body into the wash house by threatening to implicate him in the death of his wife if he did not agree – a threat which even the illiterate Evans would fully have understood. But when Dr Donald Teare carried out a post mortem on Mrs Evans, he found no evidence that an abortion had been attempted. Mrs Evans had not been gassed but strangled. In retrospect, it would seem to be asking too much even for the ordinary man, let alone the suspicious police,

to believe that two stranglers could be operating in one tiny tenement. Christie, although known to have an old record, had been a
policeman himself. That seemed to clear him and, according to
police reasoning, the arrest of Evans was inevitable.

During his talk with Evans, Christie gave the impression that he
was not in the least worried about the way things had gone. When
the subject of the disposal of Beryl's body was raised and Evans
sensibly told Christie that it would be foolish to try to get rid of it,
Christie airily dismissed his fears. His plans had been made. He
told Evans to go to bed, act normally on the following day and leave
all the arrangements for the baby to him. Naturally, Evans thought
his mother would be the best person to look after the child but
Christie overruled him. He said he had a young couple in mind in
Acton who would be delighted to take charge of the child. Two
days later, Evans was told that the couple had taken the child and
everything would be all right. Such was the domination of Christie
over his neighbour that Evans did not say another word. He seemed
to have been fond of the baby but perhaps he was glad an awkward
problem had been solved, though it is doubtful whether he would
have been happy about the solution.

Evans was undoubtedly his own worst enemy but only just, when
Christie was around. If he had not inexplicably run off to Wales,
the whole chain of events would not have occurred. He would have
had no need to have confessed to the police, for even he must have
known that any reference to 10 Rillington Place in connection with
a violent death would automatically have aroused police interest in
the house and resulted in the finding of a body. Even if he had not
committed the murder himself he was, at the very least, an accessory.

The police at Merthyr Tydfil did not quite know what to make
of the little man who talked so volubly about grave matters like
murder, but London policemen who had been informed by telephone of what he had said took the precaution of searching the flat
and, on the strength of a stolen briefcase they found, Evans was
put under arrest and taken to London.

Mrs Evans had not been seen while the search was going on but
Evans had said she had gone to either Brighton or Bristol and his
explanation of her absence was accepted. But the police decided
that a thorough search of all the rooms at No. 10 was justified and,

inevitably found the bodies of Mrs Evans and her baby in the derelict wash house. Both had been strangled and, judging from the bruises on her face and body, Mrs Evans had been beaten up as well.

Evans had been held incommunicado by the police and knew nothing of the discoveries at No. 10. When he arrived in London, Christie had already spent the best part of the night at Notting Hill Police Station and, after offering all the help he could, had apparently cleared himself. Evans cannot have been altogether surprised when he was shown his dead wife's clothing but seemed to be rather upset; when he saw the cheap tie with which his baby was said to have been strangled, he almost broke down. A normal man's reaction – if he was really innocent of murder – would surely have been anger at the duplicity of his friend, who had lied and apparently killed the child he was supposed to have been seeing into the safe custody of a young couple. Certainly he would not have been fired by any desire to protect him. But Evans' reaction was immediately to admit responsibility and the words tumbled from his lips in a rush, as though he felt the urgent need for confession.

The legal proceedings which were to bring Evans to the scaffold followed the allotted course. First, the police charge and the usual reply of guilty men : 'Yes, that's right,' though Evans said nothing to the charge that he murdered his baby. Next, the committal from the Magistrates' Court during which Evans' mother was allowed to talk to him. He sent a message by her that he wished to see Christie : 'He is the only one who can help me,' he said. Christie refused to go.

Then came the remand to Brixton Prison to await the final trial. He was one of eighteen prisoners who messed together, including the notorious Brian Hume, whom Camps was to know at his trial for murdering the car dealer Setty. 'You have to watch Hume,' was Evans' verdict on him. Evans seems to have been completely unaware that his own supposed crime was as atrocious as Hume's. He contentedly passed the time playing games and, with an eye to the future, filling in his football pools coupon. Murderers on remand are traditionally brooding, melancholy, remorseful men; Evans was none of these things.

There were technical reasons why the Crown decided to proceed on the charge of murdering the baby only. The legal fiction is that all the facts of a case must be presented impartially. But, of course, in many cases, especially those where a wide public interest must be protected, the prosecution strive hard and use all the means open to them to win. Tactics are important and the lawyers in court knew, though probably Evans did not appreciate it, that the decision to charge him with the murder of his baby only did not mean that evidence could not be introduced about the murder of Mrs Evans. It is true that there was no actual murder charge in the case of Mrs Evans, but before the real proceedings started Mr Justice Lewis ruled that the two murders were one deed, in spite of the fact that they had probably been committed with a two day gap between them. A ruling the other way might have made a lot of difference to the defence.

The late Miss Tennyson Jesse, who was present at the trial, wrote of the difficulties under which the defence laboured. 'It is difficult ... to re-create the atmosphere of antipathy with which the case for the defence was received ... the whole Court despised and rejected it.'

The chief witness, Christie, who might have had everything to lose ultimately if Evans was not convicted, did his utmost to make sure that he was. On both small and important matters, he disputed Evans' statements. He did it with such conviction that he convinced the jury that his evidence was correct. When it came to the time for challenging his own *bona fides* as an honest man, defence counsel did so almost apologetically. The admitted truth, that he was not the paragon he seemed to be, made no difference to his credibility.

Counsel continued to spell out his allegation that what Evans was alleged to have done had really been done by Christie, who said he appreciated that Mrs Evans had not been killed by abortion, since she was still sixteen weeks' pregnant when she died, but by strangulation. 'Do you appreciate that it is alleged that you murdered this woman?' asked counsel. Christie said he did. 'And that you strangled her?' 'Yes, I was informed of that.' 'And that you strangled the baby?' 'Yes, I was told that.' A few more routine questions and Christie left the box with the air of an honest man who had spoken the truth and been outrageously attacked for doing so.

Evans' chief difficulty when he went into the witness box was that he had to admit that parts of his confession were untrue and parts incomplete. Any man who said he had put his wife's body down a drain would be regarded with revulsion by an average jury, whether the statement was true or not. Manifestly Evans' story was not true and Chief Inspector George Jennings told Evans he did not believe it. 'It would take three men to lift the manhole cover,' he said, looking the puny Evans up and down. Then why did he say he had done so? 'That is what Mr Christie said he was going to do with the body,' he replied.

The basis of his statements was that all he had said and done had the one motive of protecting Christie. If Evans was now speaking the truth, he had been, on his own showing, remarkably indifferent to what was happening to his pregnant wife. Evans' attitude to her pregnancy was that she had had one child and another would not make much difference. He knew that his wife and Christie had made arrangements for the abortion to take place early on the morning of 8 November 1949, and when he met Christie on the stairs as he was going to work at 6.30 a.m. he told Christie that everything was all right, just as his wife had asked him to do. The question of staying with his wife while the operation was done did not seem to arise. When he returned home in the evening, he found his wife was dead.

Some of the evidence Evans gave was palpably untrue. Dr Teare, one of the three best pathologists in England, whose evidence was, of course, accepted without question, had said that death was due to strangulation.

Evans described how he had found the body and began to talk of the blood he was supposed to have seen – blood from his wife's nose and mouth on the pillow-slip, blood from the top of her legs on the eiderdown. There can have been no blood. The sight of the dead body, with or without blood, did not appear to cause Evans much grief. After he had looked at it, he merely picked up the baby from her cot, took her into the kitchen, made a feed and gave it to her. Christie, who was already in the kitchen, told Evans to stay there and shut the door. Evans, who had a violent temper, did not remonstrate with Christie, nor fly into a rage, as he might have been expected to do. He simply complied. About an hour later, he heard Christie on the stairs 'puffing and blowing', and found him trying to shift Mrs Evans' body from the bedroom to an empty flat in the tenement. After he had helped Christie to move the body, Christie told him to go to bed as usual and Evans said he never saw his wife's body again.

Evans began to change his ground a little when he was asked to explain why he had not denied responsibility for the baby's death immediately he was arrested. It was not merely to protect Christie, he said, but because he thought that if he did not make a statement the police would take him downstairs and start knocking him about. This sort of talk sounds nonsensical to most people but it must be remembered that men of Evans' type do not necessarily look on the police as their best friends. But even if Evans had been genuinely frightened of a beating, his fright need not have resulted in a story full of fantasy, which he had to deny and which, in the end, put a rope round his neck.

His story of a violent row with his wife over money could well have been true because bruises were found on her face and neck. It could also be true, as he said, that when he discovered that his baby was dead, he did not care what happened to him because he had loved her. The whole weakness of his position was that he had confessed to the murder of his wife five times to five different people in different places. On some of these occasions, he had not been told that the baby was dead.

The last few minutes that Evans spent in the witness box were gruelling. All the lies he had told were paraded and admitted to be lies. The judge, a sick man, became testy and, when Evans wriggled and squirmed, told him sharply to answer the questions. Christie had said that because of his acute fibrositis, he would have been incapable of carrying the baby, let alone of dragging Mrs Evans' heavy body along a narrow passage. 'I still say I helped to carry my wife's body,' said Evans. Could he suggest why Christie should have strangled his wife? 'Well, he was at home all day,' was the lame reply. Lie was piled on lie, refutation on refutation, and, in the end, Evans found that the prosecution's trap had snapped shut and he was inside.

Mr Christmas Humphreys did not waste words in his final speech for the prosecution: he must have felt that the jury thought Evans was as good as guilty when he left the witness box. It was probably

73

the shortest closing speech in a murder trial in modern times and the only reason Mr Humphreys made it at all was that the case was very exceptional. He asked why Christie should have strangled Mrs Evans – because he had tried to help her to perform an abortion? 'It is bosh!' said Mr Humphreys. 'Even if Christie had been responsible for the woman's death, why should he two days later, go up to that flat and strangle, unknown to this man [Evans], an innocent little baby lying there, fourteen months old? Even this fluent liar ... cannot invent an answer to that question.'

Mr Justice Lewis called the case 'troublesome and painful' and emphasized that he did not think that Christie's police record made it impossible for the jury to accept his evidence. 'It would be a terrible thing if a person who has been in trouble with the police and has had a term of imprisonment passed upon him but has for years lived straight after that, should have it said of him, because seventeen years ago he was in trouble with the police, he cannot be believed on his oath and is a practised abortionist and murderer,' said the judge. As for Evans, he had 'lied, lied and lied again'. Evans had said he confessed because he was heartbroken on hearing of the death of his child and had nothing to live for. 'Very dramatic and very tragic but do you accept that?' Mr Justice Lewis clearly did not and neither did the jury, which found Evans guilty after forty minutes' retirement. Christie wept openly.

Between the date of Evans' execution at Pentonville on 9 March 1950 and the first of a series of murders committed by Christie from 14 December 1952 onwards, Christie was in a neurotic state. His fibrositis still troubled him. It was so bad that his own doctor did not think he would have been able to lift a body down two flights of stairs. His general irritability made it hard for him to accept some good-natured but noisy Jamaicans as neighbours.

His doctor did not consider he was malingering and described him as 'a nervous type ... with fits of crying, sobbing; he complained of insomnia and headaches and giddiness'. Christie said he could not concentrate and complained that he lost his memory. The doctor prescribed rest and gave him sedatives. This hardly fitted in with the latest private police view that Christie was a cold-blooded baby killer.

74

It made things worse from Christie's point of view that No. 10 had been sold to a Jamaican commissionaire and Christie could barely be civil to the black tenants the new owner had installed on the first and top floors. Christie claimed, without reason, that they were always molesting his wife.

Mrs Christie's health was also not very good and drugs prescribed by Dr Odess kept her going – phenobarbitone during the day and soneryl at night. But she improved and when Christie visited Dr Odess in March 1953 he told him that his wife had gone to stay with her sister in the Midlands. By this time, Mrs Christie had been dead for more than three months and Christie had begun a covering-up plan to account for his wife's absence.

If Christie had ever given his predicament any serious thought, he must have known it was inevitable that, if ever he left No. 10 Rillington Place, his crimes would be discovered. Someone would begin to grow flowers and in cultivating the garden would uncover the bodies there. While he continued to live there, after his earlier murders, he could take some steps to avert suspicion. There was the smell of the bodies to consider. The weather was cold but it would not always be cold and, as spring approached, Christie prudently and liberally splashed Jeyes Fluid about to keep down the smell as it became more pronounced. It was an action one of the Jamaican tenants found unusual.

Mrs Christie belonged to a family which kept in close touch by means of visits, letters and even telegrams. Christie could, and did, explain why visits and letters had stopped – Mrs Christie was suffering from rheumatism and other illnesses, and could not write, he said. But it was all short-term.

But he had more on his mind than the two women buried in the front garden – the obvious, but to others unknown, reason why he had fought to keep the garden to himself – or the deaths of Mrs Evans and baby Geraldine. There was also the body of his strangled wife lying under the floor boards of the front room and those of three prostitutes mouldering in a cupboard in the kitchen.

Why Christie chose to murder his wife is one of the great mysteries of the case. They had been married for twenty-five years and were reasonably happy, though they did not seem to have much social life. According to Christie, they had had no sexual relations for two years before his wife's death, but doctors confirm that this is not unusual in late middle-aged couples, when the sexual fires are dying down. Christie said he strangled his wife about eight o'clock in the morning when his wife, stirring in the bed, woke him up. 'I sat up in bed and saw her laid there and she seemed to be convulsive. Her face was bluish. She seemed to be choking and with what little knowledge I had of first aid, I had a try to help her to breathe again. I could not. It seemed that she had gone too far by that time, and she had gone. I didn't like to see her like that, so I put her to sleep with a stocking.'

If that explanation sounded implausible to the court, Christie's next statement could be proved a lie. He said there was a cup half full of water and a small bottle containing two phenobarbitone tablets on a bedside table. The night before, the bottle had contained twenty-five tablets and Christie left the jury to draw the inference that his wife had taken the rest. But Dr Camps, when he conducted the post mortem, found no evidence of the tablets in the stomach. 'If he [Dr Camps] is right, you must be wrong,' said the Attorney-General, Sir Lionel Heald. 'Are you sure that is the truth of what happened?' 'Yes, I am sure.'

Christie left his wife's body where it was, on the bed, for two days before he decided that its resting place should be under the floor boards of the front room. He tried to do the burial decently and covered the body with buckets of soil brought in from the garden before replacing the boards. He admitted now that he was in a 'state', and it must have been a state close to panic. It was less than ten days to Christmas, a time to which Mrs Christie and her friends all looked forward, and Christie decided he must lie low until the festivities were over. But after Christmas, he decided he must do something. He sold his furniture; there was not much to sell and all he got for it was £13. His wife's wedding ring, which he had taken from her finger as a keepsake, went to a jeweller for £1.17s. As he said, he was living frugally on his dole money of £2.14s., but out of it still bought fish and chips for his dog and cat.

By mid-January, his panic must have subsided and the killer instinct in the prim, priggish clerk revived. If Christie was to be believed, he did not need to search for his next three victims: they thrust themselves on him.

In those days, before London's great 'clean-up', prostitutes began to ply their trade at Marble Arch and they were still thick on the ground at Notting Hill, though the class was not so high there. Christie's account of his meeting with Kathleen Maloney, the first prostitute he killed, had a ring of truth. He met her in Ladbroke Grove; she was drunk and asked him for a pound for 'round-the-corner' intercourse. Christie said he was not interested and anyway had no money to throw away. Her price, instead of coming down, surprisingly went up; it was now thirty shillings, and if he did not produce it she said she would make a scene and say he had interfered with her. She followed him to his door and forced her way inside. In the kitchen she picked up a frying pan to hit him but he struggled with her and she fell back on to a home-made deck chair. It may seem extraordinary to most people but there happened to be a piece of rope lying handy. The next thing Christie knew was that it was round her neck and she was dead.

The killing of a woman, even in hot blood, can never be taken phlegmatically, but Christie did not seem unduly put out. 'I left her there in the bedroom,' he said. 'After that, I believe I had a cup of tea and went to bed.' The next morning, he washed, shaved and made a cup of tea before putting the girl's body in the kitchen alcove.

Christie's meeting soon afterwards with a virago from Ireland, Rita Nelson, was equally fortuitous. It was in a crowded Hammersmith café and he took his seat at the same table as two girls, one of whom turned out to be the then unknown Rita. Conversation began as it often does, when she asked him for a match, and Christie soon knew that the girls were looking for a new place to live. Christie said he might be leaving his own flat soon but, in any case, there was an empty flat at his house. Christie arranged for the two girls to see the flat but the unlucky Rita went alone. It was soon clear to him (so he said) that the flat was not all that took Rita's interest. Rita was a prostitute, whose prime interest was in money, but she did not mention it initially and appeared to have had bigger things in mind. Ignoring Christie's protests, she undressed and began talking of coming to stay at the flat as Christie's mistress. Christie told her to get dressed and clear off and the mood changed at once. Rita threatened Christie, told him she would get some of the Irish boys to come and 'take care' of him and, said Christie, 'Well, I strangled her.' That was a second body destined for the cupboard.

Christie met his third victim of the series outside, not inside, a local café and she was with a man. Hectorina (Ena) McLennan and her friend, William Baker, were being put out of their lodgings at the weekend and Christie played the Good Samaritan by offering them the Evans' flat. With two bodies in the kitchen cupboard and his wife under the floor boards, Christie was certainly taking a risk, as his counsel pointed out. But the risk lessened when Christie took a dislike to Baker and threw them both out after two or three days.

Miss McLennan, who in the course of her chequered life had been married to a Burmese, came back alone the same afternoon and said she was exhausted. Reluctantly, Christie let her in to see what she wanted, but when he heard she wished to return he took her by the arm and began to propel her towards the door. In the struggle, some of her clothing was torn off and some got caught round her neck. Christie said that just outside the kitchen she 'sort of fell limp, fell down in front of me'. He thought he must then have strangled her, had intercourse and put her in the cupboard, but he could not remember doing any of these terrible things.

At Christie's trial, the Attorney-General had not referred in any way to the death of Mrs Evans and it was left to his own counsel to bring the matter into the open to allow Christie to give his version of what had happened. Licking his lips, as he often did at crucial moments of the trial, his leathery face paler than usual, Christie recounted how he and his wife were concerned about the pills Mrs Evans was taking to end her pregnancy and generally about her 'haggard' appearance.

On 7 November 1949, the day before she died, Christie went upstairs to have tea with her. Christie denied that he had attempted an abortion on her but no explanation was forthcoming as to why he should be having tea with her. He said he found the place full of gas, with Mrs Evans unconscious on the floor on a quilt. He managed to revive her with tea and she made him promise he would not tell anybody what she had tried to do.

Mrs Evans invited him to call next afternoon and said she still intended to go through with the suicide. She appealed to him to help her to succeed. 'So I did,' said Christie, as though he felt he was doing her a favour. Christie said Mrs Evans had 'offered intimacy' if he would help her and admitted he tried to take advantage of the offer but his back was too sore. Still, he carried out his part of the bargain. He attached a piece of tubing to the gas and put it near her face. When he turned on the tap, he strangled her for good measure. Although pressed by both the judge and counsel, Christie continued to deny that he had had anything to do with the murder of the baby. Evans had been hanged for the murder and Christie must have known that if he now admitted the murder himself the jury would make short work of him.

Three weeks were to go by between Christie's murder of his last victim, Ena McLennan, and 31 March 1953, the day he was arrested while contemplating the Thames on the embankment at Putney Bridge. Christie may have been – and was – a brutal, sadistic killer, but his aimless movements after the murders were those of a man without purpose or guile. He cannot have thought of himself as being on the run for he seemed to have no plans to avoid arrest. He simply drifted. He had let his flat and taken rent for three months in advance, which annoyed the landlord when he found out, because Christie had no right to sub-let and owed his own rent anyway. He had booked in at a Rowton House – one of the first places the police would search once they began to look for a man without a fixed address.

On the evening of 24 March, as he was about to have dinner, Dr Camps was called to Rillington Place to begin his important part in bringing Christie to justice. A Jamaican named Beresford Brown, to whom Christie's flat had been let, was going over the kitchen prior to re-decorating when he thought that one of the kitchen walls sounded hollow as he knocked his fist against it. He peeled off some of the wallpaper and the wall was shown to be really a partly broken cupboard door. His torch revealed the ghastly sight of a naked corpse bent forward to show a large expanse of her posterior. When she was pulled out, it was seen that she had been resting on another corpse wrapped in a blanket, which in turn was resting on a third.

Top-ranking police were quickly crowding the little house and the bodies were taken to the Kensington mortuary. In the meantime, the front room had been searched, and loose floorboards had been found and prized open. The dark recess underneath was the grave of another woman. Night had fallen when Camps first arrived, and the smell of decomposed flesh, though not very pronounced, was an indication to him that the women were not recently dead. On Camps' suggestion, a police guard was put on the house and the fourth body was left where it was until the following morning.

At first light, Camps was present when the police moved it to the mortuary. The body was that of Mrs Christie, and it had been wrapped in a flannelette blanket, secured with a safety pin at the top. The body had stockings on both legs but no other clothes. The head was wrapped in a pillow case and between the legs was a vest, in the position of a diaper, as Camps put it – a feature of the other bodies. For a woman of her age (fifty-four), she seemed to have been healthy, and the cause of death was asphyxia. Camps had always held the view that determining the time of death must be in the nature of an inspired guess, backed by the pathologist's experience of similar cases. In this case he was more than usually cautious. He gave the time of death as twelve to fifteen weeks earlier, but even then added that it must, of course, be approximate.

Again, the prosecution did not introduce the other dead women into the evidence. But the defence asked Camps for the post mortem particulars and were closely concerned to know whether he had found signs of gassing. In the case of Mrs Christie, the answer was 'No', but the other three all showed signs of gassing while alive, strangulation, and sexual intercourse before, during or after death. Exactly how Christie persuaded three tough prostitutes to sit quietly in a deck chair and be gassed was never explained, nor did Christie tell the court how, in a roomful of gas he had avoided gassing himself. Only Miss Maloney, who was twenty-six but looked twice her age, had been drinking. Dr Teare has gone on record as saying that a pathologist cannot diagnose whether intercourse has taken place after death, and it is interesting to see that, in his own book about the murders, Camps amended his view on the possibility. 'An opinion was formed that intercourse had taken place *at* or *about* the time of death,' he wrote, thus refuting the rumour that Christie was necessarily a necrophile.

Camps was also able to prove from his post mortem that Christie's suggestion that his wife had taken a large number of phenobarbitone tablets was untrue. Her stomach was empty, and if she had taken a very large dose there might well have been some residual powder left, though not necessarily visible to the naked eye. But, asked Mr Justice Finnemore, would there be signs of it on close examination? 'That would be a different matter,' said Camps. 'That is a chemical examination. I think a large dose, yes.' 'Sufficiently large to give someone an indication that she might be dying or in serious straits?' Camps' answer was, 'Yes, I should have thought so.'

Three days after Camps had conducted his post mortems at Kensington, the police, who had been going over the house and garden inch by inch, made another gruesome discovery. Almost the first spade thrust into the soil uncovered a number of bones. Corpses inside the house and bones outside! Grimly and methodically, the police continued to dig and the pile of bones of all sizes grew until the diggers thought they were excavating a disused graveyard. Another important find, which gave the police a clue about the date when the bones had been buried, was a newspaper for 19 July 1943. The bones were not all under the soil. A thigh bone, weathered and discoloured, was spotted propping up the garden fence.

The police asked shopkeepers in the district to provide empty tea-chests, and the bones identified as human by Camps and the police surgeon, Dr Shanahan, were carefully placed inside. Some were so fragmentary that an assessment could not be made on the spot as to whether they were human bones or animal. A large number were definitely not human, and it soon became obvious to Camps that Christie had used the garden as a midden, throwing into it the bones his dog had gnawed and played with, as well as those from his own Sunday joints. Some bones had been blackened by fire and appeared to have been burned in a dustbin lid which was found in a hole. It also contained part of a jaw.

Camps had the bones taken first to Scotland Yard's forensic laboratory, where he, Mr Lewis Nickolls, the laboratory's director, and his staff, began the laborious task of sorting them. Bones give a pathologist many clues. They provide him with an indication of age, sex, height, time of burial and sometimes occupation. Camps quickly picked out two long bones from the pile, showing that he had two skeletons, not one, on his hands. This puzzled him because there was only one skull. But later, at the London Hospital Medical School, Professor Richard Harrison, who, as head of the forensic science department at London Hospital, was supervising Camps and his team of five doctors, confirmed that there were two skeletons. Both were women, one five foot seven inches tall and about twenty-one and the other six inches shorter and about thirty-three.

Jaw bones are perhaps the most useful of all bones in the Palace of Truth, as Camps has fancifully called his mortuary, and one of the teeth in part of the jaw bone recovered from the garden had a Palladian crown of a German or Austrian type. There was now metaphorical flesh on the skeletons and it was up to the police to match the pictures with those from their register of missing women. They had to go back a few years but the match was made without much trouble. The skeletons were of Miss Fuerst and Miss Eady. As Camps was to write on the value of co-operation between police and pathologists: 'The descriptions and identifications of Christie's first two victims are outstanding examples of what really systematic, properly controlled and directed scientific examination can yield when closely associated with good police investigation.'

Christie himself solved the mystery of the missing skull. When the bodies of Mrs Evans and her baby were found in the wash house, the police had looked at the garden in a cursory way, but finding no sign of recent digging had no reason to give it another thought. But, according to Christie, while the police were there his dog was nosing about the flowerbed and uncovered the skull. He hid it quickly and after dark threw it into a bombed house nearby. It seems unlikely that he could have hidden it while the police were present in the small garden but it is a fact that children found a skull when playing in the bombed house and took it to the police station. A police surgeon, on the coroner's instructions, examined it and concluded it had belonged to a woman of about thirty-three, with adenoids – a description which, years afterwards, was found to fit Miss Eady.

From the judge downwards, everybody in court had been impressed by the painstaking and skilful way Camps and his colleagues had assembled the skeletons – the single skull found had been reconstructed as already stated from 110 pieces – and the clear way the evidence had been given. At the end of Camps' evidence, the Attorney-General, on the pretext of re-examining him, paid him a warm tribute. He asked Camps if the evidence put before the court, as a result of team work, did not represent a remarkable feat of investigation. 'I think it is very satisfactory,' Camps replied modestly.

Much has been made by some writers on the Christie case of a box of pubic hairs found in Christie's flat. Ordinary men do not normally keep boxes of pubic hairs at home, but the prosecution was interested because some of the hairs were those of Mrs Christie. None came from the three women in the cupboard but another set of hairs in the box had been cut from one of the skeletons in the garden and the other set from Mrs Evans. The theory has been propounded that Christie had been a hair fetishist since, as a child, he saw his mother combing his dead grandfather's hair, and was shooed away. But a quirk of that sort would scarcely justify murder to gain his raw material.

The final question remains whether Christie was, as he said, mad. Would a sane man have murdered both women he knew and women he did not, so senselessly and needlessly? Camps' theory was that Christie could reach a sexual climax only if his partner was unconscious. When he murdered it was for the sake of sexual gratification, which put him in the position of a rapist who was prepared to go further than most.

Dr J. C. M. Matheson, principal medical officer at Brixton Prison, where Christie spent his time on remand, had a vast experience of murderers and other violent criminals. He gave it as his opinion at the trial that Christie was weak in character, immature, hysterical – but sane. Dr J. A. Hobson, a well-known consultant physician in psychological medicine, who was called in for the defence, said Christie had an abnormal memory. He believed Christie knew what he was doing but thought it highly probable that he did not know what he was doing was wrong. 'I think he got some feeling of satisfaction in continuing to live in Rillington Place with the dead bodies nearby,' he said. A third doctor, Desmond Curran, a psychiatrist called by the Crown, described Christie as a notable egocentric who kept a photograph of himself in his cell. He was a great talker, cheerful and boastful, above average intelligence, polite and well-behaved.

'He has never said anything (in prison) to suggest that he was not in his right mind.' Dr Curran agreed with Dr Hobson that Christie realized quite clearly that he was killing his wife. It was the same with the three prostitutes he murdered.

Mr Justice Finnemore summed up with his usual impeccable fairness and the jury took only one hour and twenty minutes to find Christie guilty. The Scott Henderson Committee set up by the Home Secretary to enquire whether there had been a miscarriage of justice in the case of Evans reported negatively. Christie evidently also decided that he was not a victim of a miscarriage of justice and did not trouble to appeal. The last Camps saw of him was on a mortuary slab. He had just been hanged at Pentonville and Camps conducted the post mortem. In the stomach were the remains of a hearty breakfast. Although a teetotaller, Christie's last drink had been a small whisky. Camps noted sardonically that his penis was 'well-developed'.

Camps retained one memento of the Christie case that he prized. It was a letter sent to him by Sir Theobald Mathew, the Director of Public Prosecutions, recording his gratitude for and appreciation of the assistance Camps had given at all stages of 'this troublesome matter'. In particular, Sir Theobald paid tribute to the brilliant work done by Camps and his assistants at the London Hospital in the reconstruction of the bones found in the garden at 10 Rillington Place.

'Not only was the work itself outstanding but the making of the coloured diagrams of the reconstructed skeletons was a remarkable achievement that was of the greatest assistance,' he wrote. 'Please convey to the "back-room boys" concerned, of whom you were so admirable a captain, my congratulations and thanks.' The Attorney-General and the other counsel, added Sir Theobald, had asked particularly to be associated with his letter.

With his reputation now established so firmly, it was not surprising that Camps' last years were to be brilliant.

Three

Two Widows

The Mummy in the Cupboard

On more than one occasion in the course of his career, the mere presence in court of the robust figure of Francis Camps on the bench usually reserved for eminent expert witnesses caused a shudder of apprehension among those who knew he was to be called for the other side. He did not have to give evidence before this happened; as soon as he settled himself in his seat, people were nudging each other and pointing with eyes and head. A man whose occupation was to cut up bodies was, in the eyes of laymen, an awesome figure, even though he did seem soon to be on genial terms with counsel. But Camps was famous, too, a household name even in circles where that sort of fame does not count for overmuch, and an expert whose evidence could save or condemn a man in spite of evidence for or against him.

In a case which became known to criminologists as 'The Mummy in the Cupboard', Camps, with another famous pathologist, Sir Sydney Smith, was to have given evidence for the defence. Camps, who was later to cause considerable astonishment in court when it was said that he examined the bodies of an average of four mummies a year, did not give evidence. Neither did Sir Sydney, a pathologist with even more experience of mummies than Camps, since he had practised for many years as a pathologist in Egypt. There is no doubt that their mere presence in court, and the fact that the defence had been given copies of their reports, hastened the decision of the prosecution not to pursue the woman in the dock.

The victim who became the mummy was another woman and the case had its sad as well as horrific undertones.

Mrs Sarah Jane Harvey could scarcely be seen from the well of the Assize Court at Ruthin, Denbighshire, in October 1960, when she peered over the top rail of the dock to plead Not Guilty through her counsel, Mr Andrew Rankin, of the murder of Mrs Francis Alice Knight.

It is hard to say which of the two women concerned in the case was the more pathetic. Mrs Harvey was, for all to see, a tiny, inoffensive-looking, grandmotherly figure, who before her appearance in court had alternatively fluttered and cooed her way through life. In the old phrase, she did not seem as though she could have hurt a fly. From time to time she took in lodgers at her home in a terrace of small houses at the seaside town of Rhyl in North Wales. Mrs Knight was the wife of a respected Rhyl dentist. The marriage had withered away by 1936. The dentist had left her to live in Hove, Sussex. Mrs Knight remained in her home town and took a bed-sitter in Mrs Harvey's little house. Both women lived near the poverty line. Mrs Harvey had her pension and 30s a week from her lodger, Mrs Knight. Mrs Knight, through the courts, received £2 a week from her husband and also relied on her old-age pension.

But, if their incomes were low, their lives were in any case circumscribed and their material needs small. Mrs Harvey suffered from a variety of the complaints that accompany advancing years and Mr Justice Davies, the trial judge, said the medical reports showed that she was a very sick woman. Mrs Knight was lame from disseminated sclerosis but the disease did not seem to have reached anything like its killing stage. She also had kidney disease. But she certainly did not behave like a chronically sick woman. According to a friend who saw her regularly before her death, she was cheerful, retained her sense of humour and never complained of pain, though as she was frightened of over-balancing she usually walked with a stick.

Appearances were unusually deceptive in the case of Mrs Harvey. On her own showing she was a cool and accomplished liar. She was elderly but had nerves of steel. She was heartless and knew the facts of death as well as of life. She was greedy and the prosecution said she was something worse – a murderess who had killed an old friend for the sake of a small weekly amount of money her death could bring in.

The discovery that Mrs Knight had died what the prosecution alleged was a violent death came twenty years after it occurred.

86

Old women, as well as old men, forget but Mrs Harvey at her trial said she had never forgotten what had happened. She said she had been through hell. But if she was an innocent victim of circumstances and her conscience had troubled her all that time, there would have been a simple way out. Immediately Mrs Knight's death had occurred, she could have gone to the police station at Rhyl and told her story. Pathologists could have corroborated – or disproved – it. She preferred silence, and looking dispassionately at the evidence provided by the twenty-year-old mummy, though untested by cross-examination, the authorities decided to prosecute.

The mummy might have lain undiscovered for many more years if Mrs Harvey had not had a good son. Leslie Harvey was a taxi-driver, who in his spare time was a handyman. In April 1960 his mother went into hospital for cancer tests and he decided to clean and paint her house in readiness for her return from hospital. The house had been his home until he had married two years before. He still had a key and after work called to make an estimate of the amount of paint he would need.

He left his wife to look around downstairs, climbed the carpeted stairs and, at the top of the landing, paused in front of a two-door, ceiling-to-floor locked cupboard made of pinewood. It had often aroused his curiosity as a lad. Once his mother had caught him trying the lock and had told him off. 'There's stuff in there that belongs to those London people, the Whites – or was it the Wrights – who lodged here at the time of the blitz,' she said. 'They will pick it up one of these days and kick up a fuss if the cupboard has been interfered with.' It became an accepted fact of his life that the cupboard always remained locked but now he decided to investigate.

He had a screwdriver in his pocket and forced the door. A wave of dank air hit him in the face as he pulled the door open. Leslie shone his torch through the lacy cobwebs which drooped from the walls and hanging fly-papers and obscured the flowered wallpaper. He then saw something that shocked him. A brown human foot protruded from a small mound which lay under a mouldering blanket. Leslie shut the door quickly, called to his wife as he ran down the stairs and together they rushed to her father's house a few streets away. The two men returned to take another look into the cupboard. 'It's a body,' whispered Leslie Harvey to his father-in-law. 'Whose can it be?'

Soon afterwards the Rhyl police surgeon who was peering into the cupboard realized immediately that, no matter whose body it was, a doctor with more experience of such things would have to make the first thorough medical examination. He could feel there was no flesh on the body; it was as hard as a statue, as Dr Edward Gerald Evans, the pathologist who examined it first, was to say in court. Not only was it rock-hard but it was stuck so fast to the floor that it might have been riveted. A garden spade was needed to free it.

Dr Camps did not come into the case until after Mrs Harvey had been committed for trial by the Rhyl magistrates on a murder charge. But later Camps gave his approval of all the steps taken by Dr Evans after the mummy was found. It is true that for effect Camps made the impish comment later on in the prosecution that, in addition to the title 'The Mummy Case', there might have been added the phrase 'bricks without straw'. That was, however, hardly the fault of the pathologist concerned, who did not decide himself whether a prosecution should be undertaken. In fact, Camps praised the care taken by Dr Evans during his examination, which resulted in much fresh scientific knowledge coming to light about mummies.

The evidence given in court was that the body of Mrs Knight was in a deplorable condition – a 'shell of skin and bones' as Camps called it – after its long incarceration in the landing cupboard. The first task of freeing the body was nauseating and difficult, because every time the mummy or other contents of the cupboard were touched clouds of dust rose to choke doctors and police as they probed by the eerie and inadequate light of hand torches.

Once the dust, dead flies, spiders and rotting clothes had been carefully brushed away from the mummy, it was seen to be a woman's. The skin was maggotty, there was hardly any hair on the scalp, no teeth, tongue, eye-lashes, stomach or blood vessels. Generations of fly larva, which eat the internal organs, and the clothes moth, which nibbles away the clothes and hair, had had a long feast.

Yet what was left yielded many facts. Using two of the then latest scientific formulae for estimating the height of a body in life, the pathologists judged the mummy had been about five feet four inches

88

tall. She had been right-handed and limped. She was between fifty and sixty-five. Her blood-group was most likely to be A and the famous neurologist Sir Francis Walshe deduced from the position in which the mummy was lying that she suffered from the last stage of disseminated sclerosis. Lord Cohen of Liverpool, who specialized in the disease and had himself diagnosed it in Mrs Knight, said she might have died from that alone very soon after she had died violently.

But the most significant fact about the examinations of Evans, Camps and Smith was the discovery of a groove, or 'collar', and what could be deduced from it. No one disputed that the groove was made by a stocking, though the fragments, amounting to two inches and exhibited at the trial in a test tube, did not look like parts of a stocking. Evans said it was quite impossible to say whether the stocking had been put round the neck before or after death. Camps and Sir Sydney, from their unrivalled experience, had more definite opinions. In their reports, they said it was not a homicidal ligature; in other words, it had not been put there to strangle Mrs Knight. They said it was post mortem change with swelling which caused the groove.

Evans, the first pathologist in the field, would not agree that what he had seen round the neck was a natural ligature or fold caused by post mortem changes. Nor did he think that his comparative inexperience of such cases had led him to the wrong conclusions. He scoffed at the defence counsel's claim that Camps saw an average of four twenty-year-old mummies a year but agreed that he had seen only one other mummy before he examined that of Mrs Knight.

Camps later reiterated his claim. '... it is not uncommon to see in any coroner's area, the bodies of people who have not been found until several days, weeks or even months have elapsed after death. The evidence suggested that following death the usual process of putrefaction took place. The eggs of flies were deposited and hatched and the larvae devoured most of the soft tissues. At the same time the skin slowly dried, producing a "cast" of the position of the ligature.'

To the obvious question why there should have been a stocking round the neck at all unless it had been used by a murderer, Camps had a ready answer. It was an old wives' remedy in many parts of the country for curing a cold. The dirtier the sock, the quicker the cure, he said.

When the defence solicitors sent Camps the papers in the case and asked him, among other things, whether it was possible that the mummy might have been someone's other than that of Mrs Knight, his answer was 'No'. Too many coincidences were involved. Mrs Knight had lived at 35 West Kinmell Street as a lodger, her physical description matched that of the mummy, her teeth had been extracted many years before and she had suffered from the same known diseases as the mummy had.

The defence had been toying with the possibility of mistaken identity for a curious reason. Through the years that Mrs Knight's body was being turned into a mummy, her alimony of £2 a week had been collected unfailingly for her by Mrs Harvey. After Mrs Harvey had originally produced Mrs Knight's authority to collect it for her because of her own ill-health, the staff of the Magistrates' Clerk's office doled the money out without question. They had known Mrs Harvey all their lives and often asked after her lodger's health. Mrs Harvey was cunning enough to give the impression that Mrs Knight had her ups and downs. The authority to collect could not be found when the police asked for it but the office staff said it must have been produced before the first payment was collected by Mrs Harvey. If the money had been collected by an honest woman for Mrs Knight, it followed that Mrs Knight was alive. The prosecution did not accept what they regarded as naive reasoning. A more realistic view was that the mummy was Mrs Knight, who had died twenty years before, and Mrs Harvey had continued to draw the alimony for herself, notwithstanding that it was a weekly reminder of the murder she had committed.

Mrs Harvey was quick-witted but also stupid enough to stall when the police arrived at her hospital bed to question her about the mummy. She knew that whatever story she told would have to be good. But first came the play-acting. She pretended she was as surprised as the police at the news. But, unknown to her, Leslie Harvey had been thinking about the lodgers his mother had had over the past twenty years and had recalled to the police a Mrs Knight, a little crippled woman. The name now jogged Mrs Harvey's memory. She could hardly pretend she did not know her when she was supposed to be drawing her alimony, as an act of friendliness, and posting it to an address in Penymaes, Llandudno, where Mrs Knight now lived. A few police enquiries at the exact address Mrs Harvey gave them exploded the pitiful lie.

After one silly lie, the police were not sure they could treat as credible the next story Mrs Harvey told. She said Mrs Knight was very frail when she came to live with her and could hardly walk because of the rheumatic pains in her knees. She had not been with her for more than a few weeks when Mrs Harvey found her at bed-time on the floor in her night-dress and coat. 'I am in an awful lot of pain and would rather be dead,' she had said.

The police noticed a discrepancy in the next part of the story. Mrs Harvey said she tried but could not lift Mrs Knight from the floor. So she dressed, went downstairs to make a cup of tea, and then returned to the woman she had so callously left on the bedroom floor. 'Mrs Knight was dead,' said Mrs Harvey. There was no one else in the house and she was scared stiff. 'I pulled her along the landing and put her in the empty cupboard,' she said. If she could pull her along the landing, she could, with an effort, have lifted her on the bed, the police thought.

For a woman in a panic, Mrs Harvey seemed to have behaved with remarkable coolness. Before she finally locked the cupboard which was to become a tomb, she hung up fly-papers and wedged an eiderdown between Mrs Knight's legs and thighs. Mrs Harvey may not have been very sensible but she was well aware from experience of the physical changes that always take place soon after death.

It is surprising that with the daunting knowledge that there was a body in her small house Mrs Harvey continued to take in lodgers. No doubt she needed the money but the risk of discovery was obviously high. For instance, the police discovered that ten years after Mrs Knight died a miner and his wife, who had lodged with Mrs Harvey, became curious about the cupboard and tried to force the lock. It defeated the miner but one day he asked why the cupboard was always locked. 'Don't bother your head about the cupboard,' said Mrs Harvey, 'there is only my best linen in it.'

The police thought her story not very plausible for other reasons.

It seemed rational enough to Chief Inspector H. I. Williams and his detectives that an elderly woman should panic when she found her lodger lying dead on the floor shortly after she had suffered from severe pains. But it did not make sense that her immediate reaction should be to conceal the body – unless she had previously thought out carefully what she knew was to happen and what she intended to do. They reasoned that the natural reaction of any normal person would be to try to summon help to deal with such a frightening situation. Or was it such a frightening situation to a woman who, according to the police, had just committed a murder?

In any case, one part of the story was probably false. Mrs Harvey could not possibly have known it but the fly-papers she said she had put in the cupboard with the body bore the name of the Derby manufacturer and had a code number which showed that they had been manufactured more than a year after Mrs Knight's death.

If Mrs Harvey's story was untrue, what were the facts about the death of the frail, elderly, suffering cripple? The prosecution said that, as part of a pre-arranged plan, the victim was murdered for the sake of money – Mrs Knight's alimony. The method: strangulation with a stocking. But a stocking used for strangulation would be bound to stretch, and whether the stocking produced to the court had stretched in causing the groove round Mrs Knight's neck was of vital importance.

The judge saw this at once. When counsel for the defence opened his cross-examination of Dr Alan Clift, the prosecution's textile expert, with a general question about the nature of fabrics, Mr Justice Davies intervened in a peevish voice. 'The allegation here is that this stocking was used by the prisoner to strangle this woman. The vital question is "Has it been unduly stretched?" That is the first question to my mind that you should have asked.' Did Dr Clift agree with the Manchester Commercial Testing House that the stocking had not been unduly stretched? He did not.

Mrs Harvey's solicitors had asked for Camps' advice on two other points. The first was whether there was any proof that she could have died violently. According to Dr Evans, there were several reasons why she could have died violently: the neck grooves, the depression on the neck and the thyroid cartilages, the ligature (stocking) and its tightness, and the evidence taken as a whole. The weakness of the case, as Camps quickly perceived, was that while these were all possibilities, there remained Dr Evans' view that the cause of death was unascertainable.

Finally the defence solicitors asked Camps what was the proof that Mrs Knight had not died naturally. To this there was an answer backed by the great authority of Lord Cohen, whose opinion was that there was more than a possibility that Mrs Knight had died from disseminated sclerosis, a natural disease.

An impasse had been reached when the prosecution's case was concluded. The fabric experts for the defence would have disagreed with the prosecution's evidence. Camps and Smith thought that the medical evidence tendered by the prosecution was wrong. The case was in its fifth day and, as counsel on both sides held an informal talk while they waited for Dr Clift to recover from a fainting fit, it was plain that even before the defence was opened the prosecution's case was dangerously weak. As the judge said, the prosecution was in no position to prove the vital point of whether the stocking had been stretched. 'There seemed to be manifold circumstances of suspicion but when one considers the evidence of Dr Evans which was given with conspicuous skill, fairness and moderation, it comes to this. He cannot say whether the ligature was put on before or after death. If it cannot be proved that the stocking stretched, then the prosecution fails.'

The case was not quite over. The cost of the defence had amounted to £3,000, due largely to the prudent engagement of Camps, Smith and the textile experts to rebut what they thought would be damning evidence. The money had been provided from private sources.

The defence admitted that Mrs Harvey had brought her troubles on her own head and the judge agreed. He stopped the Solicitor-General as he rose to resist an application for costs. It was not necessary. There would be no costs.

It seemed a complete anticlimax when two token charges of fraud concerning the maintenance payments Mrs Harvey had wrongly drawn were taken. In all she had received more than £2,000 from Mrs Knight's absent husband and fifteen months' imprisonment did not seem an excessive sentence.

The Poisoner from Windy Nook

In the excellent *Encyclopaedia of Murder* by Colin Wilson and Pat Pitman nineteen women are listed as poisoners, but, for some reason, Mary Elizabeth Wilson is a notable absentee. This is strange because Mary Wilson, a sixty-six-year-old widow from Windy Nook, a drab district of Felling-on-Tyne in the north-eastern part of industrial England, was found guilty of poisoning two men who had the misfortune to become her husband and lover and was said by a doctor to be guilty of poisoning two other men.

Camps came into the case in his role of defendant's best friend. His reputation had gone ahead but because he had to give evidence in a case at Lewes (Sussex) Assizes, he arrived a day late. This was unfortunate since it created the impression, unfairly, that the man from the south was slighting a northern court. He did not examine any of the bodies but came in as an outsider. His evidence was certainly positive for the defence but was full of suppositions. He had to admit that his theories were theories and was finally somewhat humiliated by the judge, who told the jury that they must give his evidence only the same weight as the evidence of any of the several medico-legal experts who had also given evidence.

No tears need be shed for Mary Wilson, a stout, heavy-drinking, ginger-haired, self-possessed and wicked woman who killed by using phosphorus, a poison as deadly and painful as arsenic. But the question must be asked: why does an elderly woman from a working-class background turn poisoner after forty-three years of life married to one man? Why does she use such a dreadful poison again, once she has seen its appalling effects? And why, in a small town where tongues wag with little cause, should she hope to escape gossip and later almost certain detection, after murdering not once or twice, but four times.

Mary Wilson passed for an ordinary housewife, addicted to trashy romantic magazines, which certainly would never deal with poison as a theme, earthy in a north country way and known to be grasping. That she murdered for money is beyond doubt but why should she have taken the lives of others for the paltry sums she got? Insanity might be the only reason but it was never suggested at her trial and, as she did not go into the witness box to explain or excuse her actions, we shall never know why she did it.

The moderately well-to-do had servants when Mary Wilson was a girl, and her first husband was John Knowles, son of the house where she worked, who was a labourer. Her marriage could not have been entirely happy, partly because her husband was so bad-tempered. At some period in her life, she took as a lover a chimney sweep, John George Russell, who lodged with them. When the urge to poison came, she disposed of both within five months.

It may have seemed odd to the people of Windy Nook that two men living in the same house should have died in quick succession but it passed as a coincidence. They were old men and a doctor had certified that both had died from natural causes. They were of humble station in life and the community soon forgot that they had ever lived. Between them, they left £46.

The first of the two other men Mrs Wilson was accused of poisoning was Oliver James Leonard, a retired estate agent of a bossy nature whom she met in the summer of 1957 when he was seventy-five and she was sixty-four. Leonard lodged in Hebburn-on-Tyne with a Mr and Mrs Connelly and, although matrimony was on her mind, it was not love she was after but money. Mrs Wilson put the question bluntly and crudely to Mrs Connelly: 'Has the old bugger any money?' When she was told 'A little', old Leonard's fate was settled.

Mrs Wilson was a fast worker and soon persuaded Leonard to lodge with her, but a rift occurred and three days later she was knocking on Mrs Connelly's door demanding that she should get the old man out of her house. 'He will not sign any money over to me until he puts a ring on my finger, so get the old bugger out.'

The row did not last long. Perhaps Mrs Wilson realized that marriage was the easiest way to get hold of Leonard's money and they were married at Jarrow Registry Office in September 1957. Marriage did not seem to suit Oliver Leonard. Shortly afterwards, he caught a nasty cold and became doddery on his legs. Thirteen days after the wedding, a neighbour, Mrs Ellen Russell, was awakened late at night with the news that the old man was ill. She found him on the floor, breathing heavily, white-faced, speechless and obviously in pain. That universal cure-all, a cup of tea, was made and offered to Leonard but he knocked it out of Mrs Russell's hand. This, the prosecution was to say later, was proof that he knew tea he had been drinking at the house was poisoned.

But Mrs Wilson had no pity on her old husband. 'I think he's dying,' said Mrs Russell. 'I think so, too,' said Mrs Wilson. 'I've called you because you will be handy if he does.' Mrs Wilson may have called a neighbour but she would not call a doctor and Leonard died that night. Next day she went to tell the doctor of his death. The doctor recalled the old man who the previous day had come for treatment for a bad cold and he concluded it was a case of senility. It was not necessary to see the body and he gave a certificate that death was due to myocardial degeneration and chronic nephritis. Mrs Wilson collected £50, which was all he had, and when his son, with whom Leonard was on bad terms, asked to see his father's will, she sharply told him to see the solicitor.

The second of the other old men Mrs Wilson was accused of poisoning was her namesake, Ernest George Lawrence Wilson, a retired engineer of seventy-five. Wilson had put it around that he was looking for a housekeeper, but when they met after she had written to him Wilson said it was a wife he wanted, not a housekeeper. As a prospective husband, Wilson's material prospects were not dazzling. He said he had £100 invested in the Co-op, a paid-up insurance policy and a nice home, which Mrs Wilson was to discover was a dirty council bungalow, rented for 6s. 6d. a week. But she sold up her furniture and went to live with him.

As in the case of Leonard, Mrs Wilson attempted to cover up her tracks by involving a doctor before death took place. She persuaded her husband that he was ill from eating too much liver for supper, told him to stay in bed, and called a doctor. Old Ernest told the doctor that he was not ill but the seeds of doubt had been sown and the doctor was not too surprised to get a call next day and find Ernest dead. He was surprised to find that Ernest had been dead some hours and put it down to dilatoriness, due to Mrs Wilson's age. He certified that death was due to cardiac muscular failure.

If Ernest's death a fortnight after his wedding had not aroused suspicion, Mrs Wilson's behaviour would certainly have done so. Her levity was unbelievable. To the undertaker, who came to

Francis E. Camps in 1955. *Press Association*

Francis Camps and Derek Curtis-Bennett Q.C., at the Christie hearing at Clerkenwell Magistrates Court, 29 April 1953. *Press Association*

Dr Camps (*left*) at Hadleigh Heath, Polstead, Suffolk, shortly before making an on-the-spot examination of a girl's body discovered nearby, on 20 January 1961. The body was later identified as that of twelve-year-old Linda Smith. *Press Association*

Dr John Bodkin Adams after attending a public sitting of the General Medical Disciplinary Committee at which he unsuccessfully asked for his name to be restored to the Medical Register, November 1960. It was restored later. *Press Association*

PINK STRIPED SHIRT WITH BLUE TIE

NO B POC

HEAVILY PADDED SHOULDERS

ONE INSIDE POCKET ON RIGHT SIDE

BELTED WITH BLACK LEATHER-COVERED BUCKLE, WITH CENTRE PRONG

TWO OUTSIDE PATCH POCKETS WITH FLAPS

DOUBLE-BREASTED OVER-COAT, DARK BLUE OR PURPLE, WITH LIGHTER DIAGONAL STRIPES

LIGHT B TRILBY

GREY TWEED-TYPE SUIT WITH DIAGONAL WEAVE

John Reginald Christie; showing how he would have appeared in the description issued by the police in March 1953.
Keystone Press

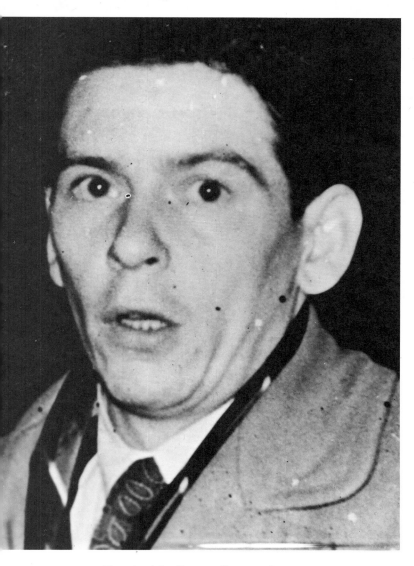

Timothy John Evans.   *Keystone Press*

Mrs Hella Christofis and
her husband Stavrous.
Keystone Press

Sergeant Frederick
Emmett-Dunne and his
wife Maria.
Keystone Press

Mrs Sarah Jane Harvey. *Press Association*

Donald Hume with
his wife.
Keystone Press

Stanley Setty.
Keystone Press

Master Sergeant Marcus Marymont. *Press Association*

(*Top left*) Ronald Henry Marwood being driven from Holloway Police Station where he was charged with the murder of Police Constable Raymond Henry Summers, 28 January 1959. *Press Association*

(*Top right*) William Pettit. *Keystone Press*

(*Left*) Edwina Taylor, aged four. *Keystone Press*

(*Far left*)
Mrs Nora Patricia
Tierney.
Keystone Press

(*Left*)
Miss Dorothy
Edith Wallis.
Press Association

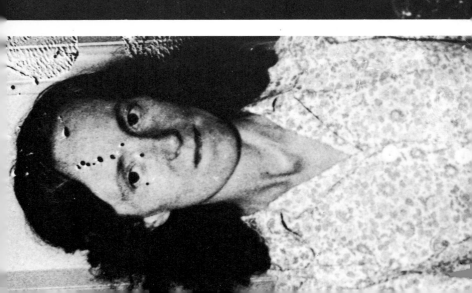

measure him for his coffin, she suggested that as she had given him so much work, the undertaker might quote her a wholesale price! She had celebrated her marriage to Ernest with a small party. 'Save the left-over cakes – they will come in handy for the funeral,' she told the caterer. Then she made another ominous remark: 'Better not save them. I might give my husband a bit longer to live.' Finally, as the net closed and she knew she was going to be arrested for murdering her two husbands, she joked: 'I didn't kill them. They were dead already.' She spent the rest of the day trying to sell her husband's gold watch and chain.

The final episode in her eccentric behaviour occurred on the following day. She told a friend that she did not fancy staying in their bungalow because her husband had gone into hospital and she would be alone. The friend said she would put her up for the night and next morning saw her back to the Wilson bungalow. As they walked up the path, Mrs Wilson gave her friend the keys to open the door observing, 'You are going to get a shock.' The shock came when she opened the door and found Ernest laid out on a trestle, ready for burial. The house was in a filthy condition. When Mrs Wilson's friend asked if she had 'done anything to Ernest', she said 'Don't be silly'.

The general practitioners who had attended the dead men had no reason to suspect that their deaths were anything but natural. When the specialist pathologists took over after the bodies had been exhumed, however, the picture was quite different. The post mortems showed that neither Wilson nor Leonard had died naturally. Wilson had no serious organic disease. Leonard's heart was normal and there was no sign of chronic nephritis. In Wilson's case, Dr William Stewart, the local pathologist, found congestion in the gullet and intestines and said the liver was yellow instead of the normal chocolate colour. But phosphorus was found in both bodies in sufficient quantities to kill. About a teaspoonful – one or two grains – is a fatal dose and, as phosphorus is not normally present in the human body, it must have been taken either by mouth, through the skin or through small wounds, though the last two were mere possibilities. 'I think they both died in the first stage of phosphorus poisoning,' said another pathologist, Dr David Ernest Price.

Even ten or fifteen years ago, few pathologists had ever seen a case of phosphorus poisoning and Dr Stewart admitted that he had never done so. But he and others knew the properties of phosphorus and Dr Price said quite definitely that both men had died from the first stage of phosphorus poisoning. And, said Dr Ian Barclay of Gosforth (Lancs.) forensic laboratory, it was not surprising, nor was it very unusual for phosphorus to be found in a body after it had been buried for thirteen months. But, to the best of his knowledge, there was no previous case quite as long as that.

Miss Rose Heilbron, Q.C., who defended Mrs Wilson, asked whether it was surprising that the phosphorus had been found. 'I don't think it is surprising for the reason that phosphorus can be protected by fatty material. In that state, its nature is preserved and sealed up.'

'It has been said that phosphorus poisoning in this case happened in the first stage?' enquired Miss Heilbron. The answer was: 'I believe that is so. Comparatively quickly.'

Miss Heilbron then asked if it was right that there was no scientific method of assessing the amount of phosphorus ingested in a body after two weeks because no one knew the rate of oxidization. 'All I can say is that I recovered yellow phosphorus indicative of the consumption of a relatively large dose,' said Dr Price.

The expert view was that either rat or beetle poison, both of which contain phosphorus mixed in a bran syrupy paste, had been used in tea or cough mixture to kill the two men. The court laughed at the fatuous suggestion that they had taken supposedly sex-stimulating pills after their marriages to Mrs Wilson. The pills had been bought by the defence for chemical analysis, although there was no evidence that either of the husbands had bought pills of that sort. 'To get a fatal dose,' Mr Geoffrey Veale, Q.C. for the prosecution, asked a witness who gave evidence about the pills, 'you would have to take three whole bottles full?' 'That is right,' was the answer.

Camps, when he reached the witness box, had not seen the bodies and based his evidence on medical and scientific reports, but he had one great advantage over some of the doctors in the case. He had seen several cases of phosphorus poisoning himself and he agreed that treatment was available for phosphorus poisoning but the treatment was better given in hospital. Mrs Wilson had, of course, made no effort to get treatment for her husband.

Miss Heilbron asked Camps what would be the cause of death in the first and second stages of phosphorus poisoning. In the first stage, said Camps, it was heart failure. In the second stage, it was due to liver failure but in addition there was also renal failure and the heart muscle and various other muscles were affected.

In first stage poisoning, death usually occurred in six to ten hours, after intense thirst, sickness, pain and prostration. In the second stage, death took longer, causing changes in the liver. He thought if Leonard and Wilson had died of phosphorus poisoning, they were second stage cases because of the changes that had taken place in the livers.

An interesting question which was of great importance to the defence was how Mrs Wilson, if she was guilty, had administered the phosphorus. Camps said that in a previous case of phosphorus poisoning which he had investigated, various ways were tested such as in beer, cider, spirits and on bread and blackcurrant jam. 'Can you administer Rodine [a rat poison] as it is?' asked Miss Heilbron. Camps answered: 'A person would have to be blind and without taste or smell. There is a cloud of vapour as soon as you open the tin. The taste is horrible.'

Camps said that if Rodine were taken in jam, a lot depended on the jam and the type of vehicle used with it. In a case of this sort, it was essential to examine the contents of the stomach to find any foreign bodies and see what kind of food had been taken. If the phosphorus had not been given in tea, there was a strong possibility it was disguised in cough mixture. Both men had similar bottles of it and one of the bottles contained a teaspoonful of Rodine. Camps was asked whether he was prepared to give a cause of death. 'The findings of the cause of death are pathologically contradictory,' he said. 'In view of the contradictory findings and in the absence of microscopic evidence, I would not be prepared to say.' But, if asked to suggest a cause of death, he would say Wilson had died from heart failure and Leonard had died from cerebral thrombosis. These were only suggestions. 'If I were asked to put a cause of death, I would put "Unascertainable".'

Camps would not say what had caused death in the case of Wilson but he did not think that it must necessarily have been phosphorus poisoning. 'I think it would be dangerous to say that because other causes of death have not been excluded.'

'What other causes could there have been in an old man of seventy-six on the findings here?' persisted Miss Heilbron. 'The commonest cause of death at that age is undoubtedly heart condition,' said Camps. 'Is diabetes a possibility?' asked Miss Heilbron. 'No, I don't think it is a possible cause of death but a possible cause of fatty change in the liver. But there are lots of other things which might be a cause of change.'

Forensic medicine does not normally deal with coincidence and Mr Veale asked Camps whether it was some form of coincidence that they were investigating the deaths of not one but two men who had something in the gullet, intestines and liver and also had phosphorus in the stomach. 'I don't think the gullet and liver have any significance,' said Camps. 'The only thing I think of any significance, which could be interpreted, is phosphorus.'

'What about symptoms?' asked Mr Veale. 'In Leonard's case there was pallor, pain, restlessness and mental change.' Camps said it was only a picture of anyone dying. But might not phosphorus poisoning have stopped Wilson's heart? 'It could have done. The only thing that worries me is that there are too many things missing.'

Camps was cautious when his attention was called to the opinion of Dr Price that the deaths were due to phosphorus poisoning. 'I would not go as far as to say that,' he said.

No one could have been defended more ably than Mrs Wilson. Miss Heilbron, her counsel, seized on any supposed flaw in the case and magnified defects that were apparent only to the defence. Much was made of the fact that the death certificates of the two men did not give the true cause of death and that the bodies had not been seen by the family doctors soon after death, which was common enough when unnatural death was not suspected. Later, Camps was to say that in a period of five years at the London Hospital, the wrong cause of a 'natural' death had been certified in no fewer than 260 cases.

Phosphorus poisoning cannot be detected without a post mortem and there was no reason why post mortems should have been held in the case of Mrs Wilson's husbands. The extraordinary suggestion

Miss Heilbron had made to Dr Stewart, a pathologist of great experience, that because he had taken sections of various organs only – small pieces of sliced-up tissue prepared for microscopic examination – the post mortems he had performed were incomplete, was indignantly denied by Dr Stewart. It was impossible, Dr Stewart had said, that the two men could have died naturally when phosphorus was found in the exhumed bodies. The truth was that Miss Heilbron was fighting a losing battle and clutched at every straw. Even Camps could not help her as much as she had wished. He said phosphorus poisoning was one of several possible causes of death but he could not exclude it as a possible cause. In view of the inconclusive nature of his evidence it seems surprising that he took the trouble to go north to give it.

At the beginning of the case, Mr Justice Hinchcliffe refused an application for two separate trials. The Crown has always taken a very serious view of poisoners and, until comparatively recently, the Solicitor-General of the day has always conducted cases against them. In the case of Mrs Wilson there was a special reason why a conviction should be secured. Hanging was abolished under the Homicide Act of 1957 but a person convicted of two murders could be hanged. Mr Veale expected that the judge would direct the jury to look at the facts of the two cases separately but the prosecution said they were entitled to look from the facts of one case to those of the other, for the purpose of considering whether what had happened was an accident. It was clear that the answer was that the deaths were not an accident but the result of deliberate poisoning.

On the facts, it was obvious that the judge would sum up against Mrs Wilson. She did not give evidence, on the advice of Miss Heilbron, and when Miss Heilbron revealed that she had given this advice she was rebuked sharply by the judge. His question – 'Has she helped all she could?' – was merely rhetorical. There were her lies and actions to consider; her attempts to sell her husband's gold watch on the day of his death and her statement to the public house landlord that her husband was in hospital when he was lying dead at home. As for the so-called sex pills, the judge said contemptuously that the jury should give the suggestion 'as much weight as it deserved'.

The jury, which really had nothing to argue about, was out an hour and a quarter. They found Mrs Wilson guilty of both murders but because of her age she was not hanged. Five days after she went to Holloway to serve a life sentence, inquests were held on her husband John Knowles and her lodger-lover John George Russell. Dr Stewart, who conducted both post mortems, said their deaths were due to phosphorus poisoning but Detective-Chief Inspector Mitchell could not produce any evidence to show how the phosphorus came to be in the bodies and open verdicts were returned. Mrs Wilson, convicted in the spring of 1958, served four and a half years in prison and died there, aged seventy.

Four

Soldiers and
Airmen

Master Sergeant Who Poisoned His Wife

The laws made by the American army governing the sexual behaviour of their troops serving overseas during wartime were
stringent to the point of being harsh. Rape on active service could
be punishable by death. Adultery or 'unlawful' sexual intercourse
was a crime in the eyes of the army. But observers have noticed
that, in spite of the severe penalties, lusty, hot-blooded Americans
often ignored the laws in the cause of sex. In courtship, imagination
is often unfettered by fact. Many of the G.I. brides who returned
to the United States after the war found that the bridegroom's
enormous 'mansion' was little more than the ancestral hovel. Some
G.I.'s, although already married, managed to get 'married' secretly
to British girls. The sex war was ferocious. I know of one G.I. who
left his 'bride', the mother of his child, a large wad of notes in an
envelope on the mantelpiece, with a note saying 'Thanks for the
memory'. She asked for him urgently at his base and was told he
had flown to America that morning. She never saw or heard of
him again.

Out of the millions of decent American soldiers who came to the
European war and its lengthy aftermath, Master Sergeant Marcus
Marymont was one of the comparatively few 'rogues'. He was tall
and good-looking, with a tooth-brush moustache, and in his late
thirties. In 1956 he was posted as a regular airman to the U.S. air
force base at Sculthorpe in Norfolk, after service in Japan and
various parts of America.

There had been difficulties between Marymont and his wife
Mary Helen, who was a few years older than her husband, but they
seemed to have had smoother relations in Norfolk, where there was

103

a good deal of social life in the American community. Marymont, as a fun-loving American, found life somewhat circumscribed, and he seized every opportunity to visit air force headquarters in Bushey Park near London for consultations and courses. Maidenhead, with its many gay clubs, was an easy run out from London and a popular night-spot with American servicemen. Marymont joined a party one night and met a young woman, Cynthia Taylor, a vivacious shop manageress, who at twenty-two had made an unhappy marriage and was living apart from her husband. Marymont, a mature man, was flattered by the interest of the young woman. She did not play hard to get and in the space of a very few weeks an affair between them was in full swing. But it was on a false basis. Marymont admitted to Mrs Taylor that he was married and had three children, but said his family were living in the United States. By British standards, American N.C.O.s are well-paid, but Marymont's expenses were high and he could not really afford even the small presents he gave to Mrs Taylor. Unpaid bills for ordinary items at Sculthorpe began to worry him, but he was either not able or not willing to change his way of life and resume his old, full relationship with his wife.

He had been deeply involved with Cynthia almost from the beginning. She told him that she had a child of three months and when the infatuated Marymont asked her to marry him, as soon as they were both free, he said he would adopt the child as his own, on marriage.

Marymont's predicament had not passed unnoticed at the base. In this case, the wife was not the last person to know that her husband was having an affair; she was one of the first. She was at a difficult time of her life and instead of the security of a happy marriage she was faced with the competition of a much younger and more attractive rival. Mary Helen Marymont could not endure a rowdy show-down and instead wrote out a short questionnaire, asking her husband whether he was in love with her or with the girl. If it was the girl, she asked what he was proposing to do about it. Marymont threw the paper in the fire. 'Of course there is nobody else,' he said, with an air of finality.

Mrs Marymont may have believed her husband for a time but her suspicions remained. Marymont, who was grossly careless about his personal affairs and, as it turned out later, extremely stupid as well, did not take the most ordinary precautions against being found out. He left an unposted letter addressed to Mrs Taylor lying around the house. Mrs Marymont opened the letter and this time realized there had to be a confrontation, whether or not it involved an emotional scene. 'Our life was always a strain after that,' said Marymont.

Marymont talked his way out of the situation. Some of the officers of his unit had spoken to him seriously about his position, warning him that, at the least, he would find himself in financial trouble, apart from any emotional involvement. He appeared to be listening to them but his mind was on other, more dangerous thoughts.

A famous pathologist has gone on record as saying that when a patient has serious stomach pains the doctors never think of poison. Nobody thought of poison when Mrs Mary Helen Marymont became ill with continuous stomach pains in the spring of 1958. She had been ill before, with long and short bouts of sickness and she was taking medicine, though she seemed to think it did her more harm than good. She was moody, depressed, unhappy and very worried about her health. It was partly because she was also worried about her private affairs that she yearned to go home for a time. But it cannot have entered her head that the cause of her trouble was poison. There is no reason why it should have done. Arsenic does not taste of anything in particular and the symptoms of arsenic poisoning are indistinguishable from those of bowel upset. Another vital factor from the point of view of the poisoner using arsenic is that, although raw arsenic cannot be bought at a chemist's shop without signing the poisons register, it can be bought in the form of weed killer. 'Most of the poisoners of the past,' Bernard Picton has written in his book *Murder, Suicide or Accident,* 'have been discovered by events unrelated to the medical findings, such as peculiar domestic or financial circumstances ...'

It proved to be true in the case of Mrs Marymont, and when the crisis occurred the trail to Marymont as the poisoner was so obvious that he himself might have laid it deliberately. Arsenic can kill quickly if the dose is large enough or it can kill as a result of a continuous series of small doses. Mrs Marymont collapsed on 9 June 1958 after she had had an ordinary lunch with nine other guests at the home of a friend at King's Lynn. Her illness seemed to fit into a pattern. No one else was ill but after lunch, at which Mrs Marymont ate little, she seemed to become very ill indeed. An ambulance rushed her to the air force hospital at Sculthorpe but a few hours later she died. Marymont, in his calculating way, had made doubly sure of her death, as Camps was to discover later. He was not content to kill her with arsenic by degrees but also gave her a large dose shortly before she died.

The death was obviously classed as sudden and Marymont, after his wife had been taken ill, was asked a number of routine questions by the doctors who attended her at the hospital. Had his wife had a similar attack before and if so when? How long had the attack lasted and what had been the treatment? Had Marymont any idea how the attacks were caused? If he had been trying to draw suspicion on himself, he could not have gone about it in a more deliberate way. The doctors had told Marymont from the start that his wife was dangerously ill and might not recover. His assistance about her symptoms was urgently needed to help them to save her life. Marymont reacted as if his wife had nothing worse than a bad cold. He began to talk to the now incredulous doctors about his own physical problems, in particular about his inability to make physical love to his wife. The doctors could not believe their ears and took a long, suspicious and contemptuous look at the glib sergeant. Mrs Marymont died the same night and the bereaved husband asked a final question which sent the doctors into consultation again. 'What is a toxic liver?' he enquired. He might have heard loose, uninformed medical talk in the sergeants' mess during the evening but no one could fathom why he asked the doctors such a question and what bearing it had on Mrs Marymont's death. But it seemed significant enough to make the doctors at the base decide that the cause of death must be sought independently. Marymont said he was against a post mortem but was overruled. It was conducted by Dr Camps, as a Home Office pathologist.

Marymont, the love-lorn poisoner, now found himself under the scrutiny of some of the world's greatest experts on poisons, including Camps. For the purpose of his trial, Sculthorpe was regarded as American territory. The American flag formed the backdrop, military officers were the judges, and the prosecuting officer in uniform, adopted the walk-about method of U.S. attorneys when questioning witnesses.

Camps was naturally not intimidated by such an alien atmosphere and soon made it clear that he was giving his evidence from unparalleled experience. As if to test the basis of his evidence, the army prosecutor enquired, somewhat superciliously, how many post mortems he had performed. Camps paused, as if making a mental calculation. 'I should say at least 60,000,' he said. Breaking the silence that followed the answer, the spectators were heard to mutter, in awed tones, 'Sixty thousand!'

Camps knew more about arsenic and its properties than most pathologists but nevertheless, to help the court, he had carried out a number of tests. The chief purpose was to try to discover whether the person being poisoned would have any means of knowing it. Arsenic could not be put in the mouth, even in diluted form, without causing a burning sensation perhaps as far down as the gullet, and Camps told the court that the burning sensation was so strong that it remained after the mouth had been rinsed. But it could be disguised. For instance, he said, it would take a great deal more than ten grains for an expert to detect arsenic in an ordinary liquid that would mask it and a very large quantity for it to be noticed in a strong-tasting drink like chocolate or coffee.

There had been some subtle and some not so subtle innuendoes during the trial that Mrs Marymont had taken the poison herself; not a lethal dose, perhaps, but enough to make her ill, receive sympathy and win her husband back. Camps, with his knowledge of the ways of suicides and those who attempted suicide, disposed of the suggestion. It was unusual, he said, for people who had taken poison and were found alive, not to admit that they had done so. 'People who take poison to get sympathy are only too anxious to live,' he said. The curious exception was that people who took large quantities of aspirin seldom admitted it.

The police forensic expert, Mr Lewis Nickolls, analysed the organs and was able to estimate the quantities of arsenic absorbed and the approximate time taken. He said a lethal dose would be between two and three grains and Mrs Marymont had taken that amount twenty-four hours before she died. Two other doses, thought Dr Nickolls, had been taken, the first one as much as six months before. The dead woman's hair provided the vital clue in dating the time the arsenic was taken. Hair, as it grows, does not lose arsenic lodged in it, and the nearer the root of the hair the shorter the time the arsenic has been in it. Mrs Marymont's hair had arsenic both at the root and nearer the tip and, with the rate of hair-growth known, scientists were able to provide the dates on which the poison had been given. The specialists were working in quantities as small as a millionth of a gramme, but their evidence was not disproved by Marymont's lawyers.

Once the scientific evidence had been given, the prosecution was able to establish easily the remainder of the case against Marymont. Stress and strain may have made Marymont dim-witted, but a man who undertakes murder has no right to be as stupid as he seemed. For no apparent reason he had drawn suspicion on himself by asking at a chemist's shop in Maidenhead whether they sold arsenic. He was told that he would need to register to buy it and the request was so unusual that it fixed the appearance of the man firmly in the assistant's mind. At the air force laboratory, he had strolled in one evening when the assistants had gone and picked up a number of bottles from the shelves. Security must have been lax, because although the bottles contained deadly poisons they were there for all to handle. A cleaner to whom Marymont spoke seemed to know that the bottles contained highly dangerous drugs. Marymont had actually mentioned the word arsenic as he handled one bottle and the cleaner blithely informed him that he 'would not have to take a lot of that', meaning, presumably, that a suicidal dose would be small. The curious conversation stuck in the cleaner's mind and came out at the trial.

The girl, Cynthia Taylor, with whom Marymont said at his trial that he had been in love but not deeply in love, may have gone into the affair originally with her eyes open but she suffered greatly for it. Marymont had kept in his desk at the base scores of letters she had written to him and they were read in remorseless detail in court to substantiate both a motive for murder and a charge of adultery.

Mrs Taylor knew all along, even when he was proposing marriage, that Marymont had had a wife, but was led to believe she was dead. She was most surprised when Marymont told her in the summer of 1958 that his wife had only just died. Cynthia Taylor was not an innocent girl but she could not believe that Marymont had lied to her persistently. Finally, she had to accept that Marymont had been living with his wife at Sculthorpe at the same time as he had been having an affair with and planning to marry her.

Mrs Taylor's divorce had not come through but she forgave the lies he had told and they arranged to marry as soon as it was possible. But it was never possible. Marymont was arrested just over a month after his wife had died. At his trial, when he was asked about his three children, he said he had not taken them into his calculations because they did not need him.

Marymont's trial lasted ten days and Marymont had the advantage of his mother's testimony. She said he had always been a 'good boy' and in Alaska, during the war, had won a medal for saving a sailor's life after his blazing ship sank. The officers trying him took five and a half hours to find him guilty on both charges. The lengthy appeal system built into American law finally ran out of steam. The last result was that the adultery charge was dismissed and Marymont's 'life' sentence was reduced to thirty-five years. Marymont was forty-one years old when he received the news in a Kansas jail.

The Dilemma

Before the celebrated Edgar Wallace became a household name, he kept the pot boiling by writing thrillers in serial form. A typical situation would arise when the hero had been trapped in a snake-pit twenty feet deep which men armed with rifles were guarding, 'The snakes were moving in, their forked tongues darting malevolently, their sinuous bodies approaching the helpless victim when ...' A journalist in Wallace's favourite haunt, the London Press Club, read this mind-chilling sentence at the end of an episode and asked how on earth Wallace would extricate his hero. Wallace advised his colleague to watch how easy it would be the following week. The journalist opened the magazine to see the solution. 'With one bound, our hero was free ...' Wallace had written.

Although a snake-pit was not an ingredient in the situation in which Albert Edward Kemp, a thirty-year-old soldier from South Benfleet, Essex, found himself, he might well have felt he was an unfortunate victim of circumstances *without* the means to free himself. An astute detective-sergeant, Ronald Sewell, was interviewing Kemp about the mysterious disappearance of his attractive, horse-loving wife, whose body was about to be found in a tin trunk. The trunk, tied up with flex, had been taken by Kemp and a soldier friend to the house of his wife's uncle at Hilltop Avenue, South Benfleet. Letters had been written by his wife's mother, Mrs Olive Dean, to a number of people including Kemp asking why her daughter seemed to have disappeared and not communicated with her. The moment of truth was imminent. The police opened the trunk and in it the body of a woman was found – Kemp's wife. She was in a jack-knife position and more sinister – if possible – a stocking was found knotted twice round her neck.

Was there – could there be – a possible and plausible reason for the situation? There was, and Camps, in pointing out what might have happened, secured the acquittal of the soldier on a murder charge.

The married life of Albert Edward Kemp, who in 1948 was living in army married quarters at Weybourne in Norfolk, had not gone particularly smoothly and Kemp put some of the blame on his wife, Audrey, whose passion for horses was greater than her passion for him, he said; it amounted to an obsession. Audrey Kemp had a quick temper, he also said, and looked down her nose at some of the army families among whom she lived. It did not make life easier when Mrs Kemp had a difficult time at the birth of their daughter. Eventually, Mrs Kemp had so much trouble handling both her sexual and domestic situation that she agreed that one way of easing the pressure would be for Mr and Mrs Chappell, her uncle and aunt, to adopt the child.

Kemp's was another of the many murder charges in which discovery of the body and consequent prosecution were inevitable. If Kemp had been able to stand back and think, he would have seen that at once. Mother and daughter were close, and in frequent correspondence. The letters stopped. Mrs Kemp, so Kemp's explanation ran, had walked out on him after a row. But where had she gone? To get a job connected with horses, he said, though where he did not know. It seemed to the police, from whom the mother sought advice, to be a thin story.

The camp milkman at Weybourne was able to fix the date of Mrs Kemp's disappearance fairly closely. He had seen her between 4 and 7 July 1953 in Weybourne and neighbouring villages, but a week later Kemp stopped the milk, telling the milkman that he was being demobilized and would be going away with his wife. He told the same story when he sold his electric cooker. To another neighbour, he explained his wife's absence by saying she was with her mother, who was ill. That was why he was having his meals in the army canteen.

When Mrs Dean became more pressing about her daughter's whereabouts, Kemp began to lie. At first he said he knew where his wife was but he was soon contradicting himself. His evasions sent Mrs Dean to the police, asking them to make official enquiries.

The summer had now passed. Kemp said he had kept quiet or told lies about his wife's disappearance because he did not want people in a small community discussing his private affairs. In the process of being demobilized, he had borrowed an army utility van to move furniture and other goods from the married quarters at Weybourne to Mr Chappell's house at South Benfleet for storage. Among his chief possessions were a number of trunks and a large wooden packing case. One of his friends, an Ordnance sergeant named Ronald Banyard, had noticed the case in Kemp's bedroom before when he called on him. The smell of disinfectant was so strong that Banyard commented on it. 'How can you sleep in such an atmosphere?' he asked. 'Oh, it's very refreshing,' was the offhand answer. But Kemp told a slightly different story to Mr Chappell when he asked him to store the packing case. He said it contained his electric cooker which had been treated with gun grease to prevent rust. There might be a smell, he granted, but it would soon wear off.

Kemp's foolish conduct continued after his wife's disappearance. He fell into the habit of visiting local public houses during the evenings, made the acquaintance of young women, and gave away jewellery that could be identified as his wife's.

Soon after Mrs Kemp's mother had asked for police help in tracing her daughter, Kemp was questioned by Detective-Sergeant Sewell, who pointed out to him discrepancies in the various statements he made. 'Your statement does not run true with the natural way of life,' the detective explained at one point.

There were obvious questions to be answered. For instance, if Mrs Kemp was not 'working with horses', and was unemployed, why had she not applied for unemployment benefit? 'Well, she could disappear,' said Kemp stubbornly. 'I had a sister disappear in 1937 and she's not been traced since.'

Sewell had thought of the possibility that Mrs Kemp had gone away with another man but Kemp dismissed it. 'No,' he said, 'she hated men.' Horses were her life and Kemp again said his wife had taken a job at riding stables in Yorkshire.

In view of Kemp's fencing, the time came for Sewell to put blunter questions to the haggard-looking soldier. 'From your demeanour and the facts of this case, I cannot get out of my mind that you know something about your wife's disappearance. Your appearance leads me to believe that you have not slept very well lately, probably from worry about the matter. Is there anything further you can tell me?' His remark ended with a hard stare that had lasted for two minutes before Kemp broke. 'Burn up my other statement,' said Kemp, 'it is not exactly right. I will make a fresh one.'

Sewell and a colleague found the packing case in the front room of Mr Chappell's house. Under a layer of brown paper was a white mackintosh and a green coat. Below these was a layer of straw, which covered the tin trunk. Inside the trunk was Mrs Kemp's body, and the pages of the *News of the World* for 28 June 1953, fixed approximately the date on which she had died. There were also letters which Mrs Kemp had written at various times to her husband.

The outlook for Kemp when on 25 February 1954 he faced Mr Justice McNair and a jury seemed bleak, since, as Camps was fond of pointing out, a man who has hidden a body, whether he is innocent or guilty, always stands before a jury in a very poor light.

Kemp's story seemed reasonable but he had to take it over hurdles. He said his wife had always been highly strung and emotional. He was used to tantrums in which she kicked and screamed, and, to control her, he always put his hands wherever he could to get a good grip and shook her. On this occasion, his hands went round her neck and she dropped at his feet. The surprised Kemp said he panicked, left the house for a while and returned to find her dead. 'Were you intending her any harm?' asked Mr Derek Curtis-Bennett, his counsel. Kemp replied: 'No, sir. I loved her. I would not hurt her.'

Kemp's colleagues rallied round to give evidence on his behalf. 'I never met anyone with such an even character and good temper,' said Sergeant Harry Bligh. 'He was a real gentleman.'

The main weakness in Kemp's story was that he not only admitted he had put the body in the trunk found inside the packing case but that he had taken some steps, at least, to get the case out of the way. He had also tied a stocking round her neck.

Mr Justice McNair put the legal issue to the jury in the simplest possible terms. The three possible verdicts, he said, were guilty of murder, guilty of manslaughter and not guilty. The judge could not see any evidence of provocation by Mrs Kemp, nor evidence which could reduce a verdict of murder to manslaughter. 'But,' the judge added, 'can you think that it is possible for a man who had suddenly faced the tragedy of his beloved wife falling dead at his feet, to get hold of a stocking and put it round her neck in order to create to the police the impression that he had murdered her? That is the central issue in this case on which you have to make up your minds.'

Why had Kemp deliberately put the stocking round his wife's neck and tied it after she had died, counsel asked. Kemp replied: 'As she was dead, I wanted to die, too. I wanted to make it look as if I had killed her.'

It was a point that greatly troubled the jury and still seemed to trouble them after Camps had given his evidence and the judge had summed up. In Camps' view, death had been fairly rapid – as Kemp had said himself – and asphyxia had played a part. The asphyxia must have resulted from some sort of pressure on the neck. The pathologist considered that there could have been manual strangulation but not with gross violence. 'Lack of bruising underneath the stocking could have been consistent with it having been put on after death,' stressed Camps.

The jury deliberated for two hours twenty-five minutes, and returned with a request for Camps' evidence to be read over to them again. This was not possible. Camps had left for another session of work and had taken with him the only transcript of his evidence.

The judge said he would help the jury by reading over his own notes and after this had been done the verdict was 'not guilty'.

An Airman Kills in His Sleep

At the beginning of 1961, Camps had the unusual experience of having his expert opinion rejected by a jury, although there was no expert forensic evidence on the other side to contradict him. It was all the more galling for Camps that the experience occurred at the Essex Assizes at Chelmsford, where he had so often given evidence before as an up-and-coming pathologist.

A man was on trial for strangling a girl. He was Staff-Sergeant Willis Eugene Boshears of the U.S. Army Air Force, the father of three children and, in his view, happily married. It was a sordid case of the rare type which gave the American servicemen stationed in Britain an undeservedly bad name. The girl involved, Jean Sylvia Constable, from Halstead, Essex, was only twenty when she was found dead in a ditch near Ridgewell, in Essex. Jean was one of the many girls who found the company of free-spending Americans more congenial than that of the local young men. She was a regular customer at public houses in several small Essex towns where Boshears drank. Boshears knew her as a casual acquaintance, as he knew many other girls. She had been to his flat when his wife was away, though his brother-in-law was always there at the time. But at his trial, Boshears denied that Jean was his regular girlfriend or that he always met her when his wife was visiting her relatives in Scotland.

On the last day of the old year and, as it turned out, the last day in Jean Constable's life, Boshears' main activity, apart from a little work at the air base at Wethersfield, was drinking. In view of his large consumption of alcohol before the killing, it is difficult to understand the assertion of prosecuting counsel that drink had nothing to do with the girl's death. Boshears, from Michigan, a Korean war veteran who had flown forty-five missions as an air gunner, made an early start that day. He rose between 6 and 6.30 a.m. and was at the base just over four hours after drawing his pay. During that time, he had breakfast at the N.C.O.s' club and a drink before and after breakfast. He left after a couple more drinks in the afternoon, taking with him a 40 oz. bottle of 100° vodka.

On the way to his flat at Dunmow – the scene of the diverting annual 'flitch' trial in which couples try to prove that they have been happily married for a year – he had one or two beers at Great Bardfield and a liberal helping of vodka with lemonade when he reached the flat. He did not stay long at the flat. On New Year's Eve he wanted company and found it in Braintree at the Bell (whisky and beer), the Boar (more whisky and beer), and the Bell again (unspecified drinks). Here, near closing time, he met Jean Constable and a man named David Sault from Leicester, and took them by taxi to his flat.

It was obvious what Sault and the girl wanted to do but Boshears invited them to fortify themselves first with his vodka. 'I am not sure,' said Boshears, understandably, 'how many drinks we had after that first one.' Full of drinks and hospitality, Boshears then showed Sault and the girl to his bedroom, bringing a mattress out to the lounge for himself. Presently, the pair emerged from the bedroom and Boshears provided another drink for all three of them.

Boshears said he did not want Sault to leave because he had invited him as a guest for the night, but in case Sault changed his mind he told him where he could get a taxi. All three then lay down on the mattress, Sault and the girl side by side. Sault said he left the flat about 1 a.m. As far as Boshears was concerned, that was all that he remembered until he felt something 'pulling at his mouth'.

'I was not awake when I first felt it,' said Boshears in court. 'It seemed to wake me up. I was over Jean and I had my hands round her throat. Jean was dead. I panicked. I started to cut her hair off. Then I took the body to the spare room and left it.' Later he dressed the girl, took the sheets and blankets off and put them in the bath to soak. 'After that,' said Boshears, 'I went to sleep.'

When Boshears awoke, the 'discovery', as he called it, of the body in the spare room shocked and scared him again. It took him two days to 'figure out' what to do with it and his decision ultimately was to put it in his car and drive around until he found a suitable place to dump it. This was the ditch in which it was found at Ridgewell.

The main question on which Camps supplied the evidence was whether it was possible or probable that a man could strangle a girl in his sleep. Camps said at first that it certainly sounded improbable. The cause of Jean's death was undoubtedly asphyxia caused by manual strangulation, with pressure applied for about thirty seconds, though Camps admitted that, up to a certain point, the question of the time during which the pressure was applied was a matter of conjecture. Later Camps was to modify his view about whether it was possible for a man to strangle a girl in his sleep. 'I would not go as far as to say that it would be impossible,' he said.

But neither Mr Justice Glyn-Jones nor Mr Stanley Rees, who prosecuted, was prepared to accept such an unusual proposition. 'Boshears would probably have felt the girl moving, even if he was half-asleep,' Camps agreed.

'He could "possibly" have carried this through without waking himself up?' said the judge incredulously.

'At least partially,' Camps answered. 'There would also be the effect on the victim. If the victim was asleep, she would wake up. Everybody consciously protects themselves,' Camps added.

The judge returned to the point in his summing up. 'Have you ever heard of a man strangling a woman while he was sound asleep?' he asked the jury, which included a woman. 'We have no medical evidence that there exists any record in all the records of the medical profession, that such a thing has ever happened. But,' said the judge, 'Dr Camps has said it might be possible. You use your common-sense and decide whether it happened.'

It seemed clear that the judge himself had his doubts. 'Is it within the bounds of possibility that Boshears could have moved from his position beside the girl on the mattress, removed the covering from her and then, straddling himself across her, catching her throat in his hands and applying pressure resulting in resistance, unconsciousness, convulsion and death, without being wakened by his own exertions?' he asked.

The prosecution challenged Boshears' assertion that he had had no argument with Jean, had made no sexual overtures and had no desire to kill her.

'In a sober and determined attempt to cover up what had happened, you carried her body into the bathroom and then into the bedroom?' said Mr Rees. 'This was a calculated attempt to hide the crime you knew you had committed?' Boshears admitted it.

'What crime did you think you had committed?' The answer was 'The logical one' and further amplification came a moment later: 'I had killed someone.'

In a short summing-up, Mr Rees alleged that as soon as Sault had left the flat, Boshears attempted to do what he intended to do with the woman. Trouble arose, she cried, she was hurt, he silenced her and she died. The judge said the verdict had to be one of only two. The strangler, in putting his hands to the girl's neck and applying pressure for such a length of time, intended to cause death or grievous bodily harm. He must have known what the result of what he was doing would be. So the verdict must be guilty of murder or not guilty of anything. 'There is no lesser verdict open to you,' the judge directed the jury.

After a retirement of nearly two hours, the verdict was 'not guilty'. On his release from custody, Boshears said he was very happy with the result of 'British justice'. But not everybody in court had agreed when the jury foreman said they found Boshears not guilty. One woman in court gave a gasp of astonishment and another in the public gallery shouted 'Why?'

Camps had given as his view that it is very rare for a defence of accidental death to succeed where a body has been concealed. An exception was the case of Boshears, the airman who claimed that when he killed he was asleep.

The case attracted widespread attention and in the House of Lords a few weeks later, Lord Elton enquired whether the government was going to bring in a change in the law to make possible a verdict of 'guilty but asleep'. Such a verdict, he said, like that of 'guilty but insane' would prevent a defendant from being acquitted.

Lord Bathurst, the Home Office spokesman, said no such change was being contemplated. The government, however, was looking into the question of whether a verdict of 'asleep' might in future be considered to be a verdict indicating some mental disorder. But nothing more was heard of this fatuous suggestion.

Five

Bare Bones

Bones in the Furnace

Murder, it has been said many times, is a comparatively easy exercise to carry out, but if the disposal of the body becomes an urgent necessity problems arise. Even when there is plenty of space for burial, such as fields, open spaces, moors and woodland, the task is seldom easy; but when the murderer is surrounded by bricks and mortar, as well as nosey parkers, it must be daunting.

As a murderer, Ernest Elmes, a factory handyman from Tottenham in North London, was an exception to this rule. He had a ready-made burial place; or, to be more accurate, a crematorium.

We do not know much about the background of Ernest Elmes and Rose Winifred, his thirty-seven-year-old wife, except that they seemed to everybody who knew them to be an ordinary suburban couple, whose married life ran an uneventful course. A neighbour, Mrs Audrey Watson, did not know of Mrs Elmes' association with another man, although she was very friendly with Mrs Elmes. Elmes' sister, Mrs Fisher, had always known the Elmes as a devoted couple. When Mrs Elmes disappeared, Elmes' cover story to explain her absence was that she had gone off with a policeman. Mrs Fisher thought this was 'fantastic'. Other relatives who knew Mrs Elmes well believed it to be completely out of character that she should have left home or deserted her eight-year-old son, to whom she was devoted.

The probable date on which Elmes murdered his wife was a Saturday in September 1953 when Alan Watson, his next-door neighbour, heard a loud shout from the direction of Elmes' bedroom. 'It was a long one,' he said, 'and from a woman.'

A few days later, Elmes went to Tottenham Police Station to report the disappearance of his wife and Detective-Inspector Arthur

Weston, who saw him, gave him a long, keen look. Elmes was in a filthy condition and his nails were bitten down to the quick, which seemed to be a fair indication of Elmes' anguish. There were scratch marks on his face but the detective-inspector could not be absolutely sure they had been made by a woman. 'I would have held Elmes there and then, if I had had a little more information to be sure,' said Detective-Inspector Weston. 'I was not quite sure. This man might genuinely have lost his wife.' Elmes' glib explanation of the marks on his face was that before his wife left he and the policeman who had eloped with her had had a fight.

One of Elmes' duties at the wire factory where he worked was to look after the boiler, and when he suggested to the factory manager, John McCave, that it would be a good idea to clean it out in preparation for winter, Mr McCave readily agreed. Elmes was usually a good time-keeper, but he had been away from the factory for the two days previously. In explanation he told the manager an unusual story: that he had had trouble with his wife and she had left him for a *sailor*.

He told a similar story to Mrs Margaret Bowers, a packer at the factory, but the man he said was involved this time was a *policeman*. Mrs Bowers remembered that the same afternoon Elmes was doing something in the boiler house and said that he was cleaning out the pipes. When he lit the boiler, the stench was overpowering. 'There's a horrible smell, Ernie. What are you burning?' she said. His answer was that he was burning some sacking. Elmes was actually cremating the body of his wife.

There was, of course, a girl in the case, although she knew nothing of Elmes' murderous activities. She had been an ambulance driver and had met Elmes while they were attending first-aid evening classes. Elmes had told the girl that his wife had left him for a policeman and said that he was living at home with his mother. For some reason, the girl did not believe that his mother was living at the house but she did believe the part about his wife. Eventually they began to go to the cinema together once a week, the meeting for the following week being arranged when they met. At first there was nothing more than friendship between them, but one Sunday her scooter broke down and she went to Elmes' house to ask him if he could repair it. He told her to bring it round and did repair it. She added at the inquest on Mrs Elmes that they were downstairs for most of the time.

Mr Ian Milne, the coroner, queried this statement. 'Most of the time?' he asked. 'Well,' said the girl, 'he took me upstairs.' 'Was this more than friendship?' asked the coroner. The answer was 'Yes'.

The girl went to Elmes' house on the following Sunday, after Elmes had told her that the police had been to see him about his missing wife. She knocked on the door again and again and, as she could not get a reply, she broke in through the kitchen window and found Elmes dead.

Neighbours had finally reported to the police that Mrs Elmes was missing and a detective-sergeant had seen Elmes. After closely questioning Elmes, whom he suspected, the sergeant had told him that he did not think another man was involved.

The police questioning of Elmes must have convinced him it was only a question of time before he was arrested. He gassed himself, leaving no explanation behind. At the inquest, nothing was said about Mrs Elmes, except that she had disappeared and no one knew where she had gone. But when the police searched the house they found bloodstains in various places – on the stairs and cupboards, on the living room and kitchen walls and on the linoleum. More sinister still, there were bloodstains on a hammer and efforts had been made to wash down the walls.

When the bones were found in the boiler house, Camps was able to help the police to tie up most of the loose ends of the case. He supervised their removal to the London Hospital and, after a preliminary examination, asked for a further search to be made of the boiler. 'They are the bones of a woman, but the skeleton is incomplete. You must find the skull, spine and pelvis.' The police scraped the boiler again but found no more bones.

Camps was sure it was a case of murder when he found that the bones had been cut across with a saw. The work had been done with a number of bloodstained hacksaw blades which were found when Elmes' house was searched.

The North Middlesex coroner returned a verdict of suicide against Elmes and, on Camps' evidence, a verdict of murder against Elmes was recorded at a St Pancras inquest. What was never established was how Elmes transported his wife's body from his house to the factory where he burned it.

Bones from the Graveyard

As so often in the past, Camps enlisted the help of his friend Professor Harrison to solve a riddle presented by the Metropolitan Police when, late in 1953, builders found a large number of bones on a site being excavated near the Kensington public library in West London.

The bones did not seem to be very promising material for a reconstruction of a skeleton but Camps inspected them carefully and ordered them to be taken to his room at the London Hospital for cleaning. Camps and Harrison, from a preliminary inspection, came to the conclusion that the bones had been buried for between a hundred and two hundred years – possibly more. All bones whose ages can be estimated at over a thousand years show a degree of destruction which varies, but experienced pathologists can judge age largely from experience, and the state of the bones that had been found made it likely that the bones had probably been buried no more than a fifth of that time.

Camps decided after an initial inspection that the bones were undoubtedly human, and in the next few days he was frequently in his friend's laboratory, watching and helping to sort them out. The bones were like the pieces of a gruesome jigsaw puzzle, the only difference being that the pieces had to be fitted into a number of puzzles instead of only one. In the end, the pathologist decided there were seven skeletons, of which five were between sixty and seventy years old. All were men. Only the right parietal bone of the sixth skeleton was recovered and it was impossible to tell the age or sex of the skeleton from which it came. The seventh skull was that of either a prematurely born infant or a foetus.

The most interesting feat of reconstruction was done by Camps and Harrison on the fifth of the skeletons they handled. The skull was in a number of pieces and could only be partially reconstructed because the lower jaw and part of the facial skeleton were missing. But the doctors were able to reconstruct the palate, or bony roof, of the mouth, and a single and much-worn tooth was found. The rest of the teeth were judged to have been missing for many years before death. 'These bones are graveyard remains,' Harrison said to Camps, who agreed with his opinion. There could be no other conclusion, in view of the number of skulls and bones from separate individuals who, although all elderly, were of varying ages.

Bones were constantly being unearthed in London in the years after the war, when the clearing of bomb sites was going ahead rapidly. Some of the bones, as was known, came from disused and disturbed graveyards, of which there were quite a number in London. Other bones were in small groups, where there had been direct hits and the victims had been buried under tons of rubble. Single bodies, usually of infants, were also found, and Camps always gave his full attention to the bones of such small mortals who had died mysteriously.

In July 1948 Camps was called by the police to the dreary Inner London borough of Kentish Town, to inspect a small pile of bones which had been found when the ground behind a small Anderson shelter had been dug over by Detective-Inspector Shewry and his men. Most of one pile of bones were those of birds but there was a child's femur, and a second pile contained seven human bones as well as more bird bones.

Camps had the bones taken to St Pancras mortuary and as there was no great hurry – the bones had been there for some years – he examined them at his leisure. His confirmation that there were human bones among the finds caused the inspector to ask Camps if he would be present when the ground was dug over again. This time thirty-four bones were unearthed and fragments of thirty-four more, one of which was definitely human. On the third day of the digging, Inspector Shewry recovered fifteen bones and fragments from birds and seven more bones which Camps found to be human.

Camps now had something to show for the work of the digging policemen; twenty-one pieces from the skull; thirty-seven halves of vertebrae from the spine; fifteen complete ribs and five fragments; nine bones from the upper limb and two fragments; pelvis, thigh and shin bones; plus six small bones of the hands and feet.

The bones made a child's complete skeleton and, as the length of a full-term baby varies from nineteen to twenty-one inches, it followed that the skeleton was either a full term baby or just before full term. Camps could not determine the cause of death or whether the child was born alive. He reported that it was impossible to be definite about the exact time the body had been buried but it would be in keeping with five or six years ago – a time in history when the lives of millions of others all over the world were hanging in the balance.

Camps had a number of favourite aphorisms, one of which was that at the scene of any crime nothing, however unpromising, must ever be thrown away. The crime in another case had happened before the war; it was probably murder and the remains were those of one of many infants which Camps had to examine in the course of his daily work. The 'unconsidered trifle' found by Camps among the bones and clothes appeared to have nothing to do with pathology. It was a button and it had come to light with the bones when a bomb fell into a London back garden. The owners were two toughish, elderly ladies, a mother aged about eighty and her daughter, who had lived most of their lives in the house and did not seem unduly perturbed by the bomb incident.

Camps, with his nose for the unusual, sensed that the button was a clue to something more, although to others on the spot it seemed to be just a button. Even in small matters, Camps believed in asking for the help of experts in their own fields and he sent the button to the head of the textile department of the Victoria and Albert Museum, asking if it could be identified. Camps greatly admired the way in which Mrs Ginsburg produced, not only the information he wanted, but much more besides. The button, she said, dated from the year 1920, when it was most fashionable. It was usually used on a particular type of baby's garment, but in this case the button had been transferred from the original garment to another of a different type, which Mrs Ginsburg was also able to describe.

Armed with the result of this superb fashion detective work, detectives paid another visit to the elderly ladies. They pointed out that the bones of babies were not normally found in London back gardens – Camps had given the detectives a rough estimate of the age of the bones – and asked if there could be an explanation of how they came to be there. There could. Many years before, the daughter had had a love affair and as a result had had an unattended still-born child. The simple way out had seemed to put the body in a hole in the garden and hope it might never be discovered. It was an almost forgotten episode in the lives of the elderly women and the police, prompted by Camps' wise advice about the difficulty of identification, decided that the compassionate thing to do was to forget it.

The Skeleton from the River

Boys who have vivid imaginations do not always expect the stories they take home to Father to be believed without qualification. Father has usually heard them all before. Father, in this case Mr William Frostick of Wivenhoe in Essex, had not heard it all before but found his son's story a bit far-fetched. Briefly, his son Tony and a twelve-year-old friend, David Young, who was described somewhat ponderously in a police report as 'a scholar', said they had been boating down the River Colne from Wivenhoe Quay towards Alresford Grange and had left their boat fast in the mud to walk across the flats towards Brightlingsea railway. It was low water and an ideal time for a mud-lark. The expedition took an even more exciting turn when they noticed a large bone sticking out of the mud about five yards below high water mark. Another similar bone was close to it. 'We formed the opinion,' said Tony Frostick using 'officialese' which he could hardly have invented himself, 'that they were part of a human skeleton. We did not disturb the bones unduly and left the scene to return home.'

Mr Frostick slept on his son's story but before eight o'clock the following morning was telephoning the police at Wivenhoe to report what the two boys had seen. Later on, when a police constable had collected the boys they showed him where they had seen the bones. Tidal water was covering the spot at the time and, as it was late afternoon, and the tide was coming in and the light was fading, the policeman and his colleague decided to leave the hidden bones until the following morning. The bones had not been moved at seven o'clock next day and the policemen salvaged them, cleaned off the mud and, on instructions from the coroner, sent them to Camps.

The pathologist had some facts to work on but they did not help a great deal. The skeleton had been lying on its back and would always have been covered by at least three feet of water when the tide was high. The skeleton appeared not to have been moved since the flesh had finished decomposing.

Camps was hard-pressed at the time, though he was in constant touch with the London Hospital laboratory, but he was surprised when he heard that two different opinions had emerged about the bones. When the reconstruction had been completed, no bones had been left over and it was evident to experienced pathologists that only one skeleton was involved. The skeleton's skull was small, and the contour of the forehead was smooth, round and high. It was that of a female and the height was worked out by an accepted pathological formula at five feet two inches.

Pathologists do not always claim to be infallible but Camps was more than a little bewildered when he received a further report on the skeleton, which he had taken himself to the London Hospital. He was informed that the individual was 'definitely a man' of about five feet two to three inches in height. It was possible, said the report, that the man was only fifty years old but far more likely from X-ray observations that he was over sixty. 'The appearance of the bones ... suggests that the individual had been in the river mud probably over three years but not twelve years. You will understand,' the laboratory report concluded, 'that this last remark can only be a hazardous guess but we do have a feeling that the bones are fairly recent.'

That might be so, but were the remains those of a female, as the first, extensive report had suggested? The point was cleared up to Camps' amusement when he received a letter which stated that in a covering letter with the pathological report the sex had been given as male – which was 'evidently a typing error!'

The 'Barnacle' Skull

A human skull of a young person, which formed part of an almost complete skeleton found on the beach on an August day in 1953 at St Osyth, not far from the popular seaside resort of Clacton, set an intriguing puzzle for Camps and the back room laboratory men who worked with him. How long had the skull lain on the sands after it had been washed in from the sea? How did it come to be broken in two? Had the skull really been washed in by the tides or had it been deposited on the beach in the place roughly where it was found? How could a young person be missed from his family circle without an extensive search being organized? Finally, a question of great importance: what was the sex of the skeleton?

The skull was the first part of the skeleton to be found. Mrs Alice Hazelton, a housewife, picked it up at low tide about teatime, when she was undressing on the beach for a bathe with her son. She handled it to make sure it was human and, on looking round the beach, found two more bones a yard or two away. Greatly intrigued, she made a more careful search of the area but there were no more bones and she took home those she had found. The skull and bones might have remained as family heirlooms if friends had not told her she was wrong to keep them. Two days later, she informed a passing policeman that she had them at home.

Another policeman collected the skull and bones and, for a layman, he examined them thoroughly. He noted a cavity about five inches in diameter in the top of the skull and that the lower jaw was missing. In the upper jaw there were five molar teeth, and, while the skull seemed to have been in the water for a considerable time, it was in a fair state of preservation.

Apart from Camps, marine biologists also found the skull of great interest. They called it the 'barnacle skull' because at least three separate types of barnacle were found on it. In several respects, Camps did not agree with the findings of some scientists who were not pathologists. He said the erosion of the skull was not due to sea water but to the blasting by fine sand under the action of tides and currents. The damage to the facial and lower regions had probably occurred before the skull reached the inter-tidal area where it was found, because the barnacle deposits there were thicker than elsewhere on the skull. Crabs would have eaten the flesh in a few days. Camps' sarcastic view of one of the reports he was shown was that it would not stand up to two minutes' cross-examination.

A point which was causing both Camps and Professor Harrison of the London Hospital concern was the sex of the skeleton. Harrison, after considering all the reports, said he simply could not commit himself. He advised Camps therefore to send to the authorities a very guarded report that the skull was of a young person between seventeen and twenty-one and that the barnacle population and the staining of the base of the skull suggested that it had been embedded where it was found at the bottom of the sea for about eight months. He said the skull's previous history could not be given but, from the degree of sand-blasting of the bone, suggested that the skull had probably been in the sea for some years.

It was a surprise to Camps that one of the two bones found with the skull should turn out to be that of an animal. The other was a tibia (shin bone), which may or may not have belonged to the same skeleton as the skull. Harrison thought the tibia was from a young person but it was impossible to prove that the two bones had or had not been related. He realized the difficulty of assessing sex but, although inclined to think it was female, it was not impossible for it to be the skull of a lightly built young man. The teeth were of no assistance in defining age or sex. 'If anybody cares to quarrel with this, they are welcome to do so,' Harrison confided to Camps. 'I do not think it possible to get any nearer the mark.'

The 'Monkey'

Boys do not often play practical jokes when they dig up unusual objects from a garden. As a rule, they are too excited about what they have found. But, somewhere along the line, a practical joke was thought to have been played in Kensington when twenty-six bones were dug up by a boy in the back garden of a small house. Parents and friends of the young digger did not quite know what to make of them. It was believed at first that they were the bones of an animal, possibly a dog or cat, for the simple reason that it did not occur to anybody that they could possibly be human. The bones were small and a teacher with a knowledge of zoology suggested it would be a good idea to mount them on a piece of cardboard and try to attach names to the bones. Somebody wrote on the card that the bones were those of a 'monkey' and the boy who had dug the bones up sent the card to the Natural History Museum, South Kensington, to try to get a proper identification.

The result was not what was expected. One of the senior officials at the museum took a look at the bones and said emphatically that they were not those of a monkey. It was left to Camps and Harrison to identify them as those of a newly born baby and they went into considerable detail to prove their theory. All the bones were measured carefully and they concluded that the bones were those of a nine and a half month human foetus. There were several sets of bones in the London Hospital's pathological department with which the 'monkey' bones could be compared and, after careful study, Camps and Harrison gave their opinion that the bones all came from one baby which had probably lived only a very short time.

There was not enough of the foetus left to determine its sex. Weather and other factors had caused some degree of destruction and the pathologists thought the bones had probably existed in their present form for many years. The foetus became known colloquially among those who had to deal with it as 'Charlie'. In view of the probable length of time that 'Charlie' had been dead, the police decided it would be a waste of time to attempt to identify either of 'his' parents, and the case of the 'monkey' that wasn't, was allowed to slide into limbo.

The Clue of the Dead Tortoise

More times than he cared to remember, Camps had been confronted in his professional career with a body so badly decomposed that at first he thought he could make little of it. There is a scientific limit to what pathologists can do. Camps knew there were plenty of bodies in the same decomposed state as the one the police were showing him early in 1956 – but they were underground. The body was, in fact, on top of a grave in an isolated corner of the extensive Hampstead Cemetery. At his examination of the body in the mortuary, Camps ascertained that it was that of a woman who had been dead for possibly two years. There was nothing else to establish identity because her clothes were so rotted and vermin-eaten that they fell to bits when they were removed. In the face of almost complete physical disintegration, Camps could not say what the cause of the woman's death had been.

The coroner, Bentley Purchase, and Camps inspected the body in the place where it was found and as soon as it had been lifted from the top of the grave noticed a dead tortoise which had been underneath the body. The grave was near the cemetery's enclosing wall and the two men reasoned that the tortoise might either have progressed to the grave from inside the cemetery and died there, or it might have been dead when it was thrown over the wall, to land, quite fortuitously, on the grave. Purchase, as I well knew, always took it as a personal affront if he could not establish the identity of a body brought to his mortuary and gave the police clearly to understand that he expected the mystery to be solved, and quickly.

Camps thought the more reasonable of the two theories was that the dead tortoise had been thrown over the cemetery wall before the woman died. He said a tortoise was a boy's pet and Purchase agreed. He told the police to send officers to question families with boys who lived near the perimeter of the cemetery.

The coroner's move was astute and his theory only slightly wrong. The police found a family that had had a pet tortoise but the owner was a girl. However, when the tortoise had died, her brother was left to dispose of the body and he threw it over the cemetery wall because he thought 'the cemetery was the right place for a tortoise when it was dead'.

The boy said he had done this about two years before and the logical deduction was that the woman had lain on the grave since then. Camps assessed the woman's age at about forty, give or take five years either way, in view of the state of her body. Her front teeth were slightly prominent and would have given the impression of being good and well-cared for although she probably had not had dental treatment for about six months. She brushed her teeth so well and often that they were polished and worn to a high degree. It still required patient police work to trace the young woman who had reported the disappearance of her mother about that time. The dead woman had some false teeth and, through her daughter, the woman's dentist was traced. His records confirmed her identity.

The background was tragic; another not unfamiliar case of a woman dying miserably and alone, as a result of a love affair that had ended when the woman's lover had died. He was buried in Hampstead Cemetery and after what must have been great anguish, tempered perhaps with the hope that she might meet him once again, the woman came to rest on his grave. It is unlikely that the cause of death was natural but whatever the poison with which she ended her life, Camps could find no trace of it left in her body.

Six

Women and
Children

Death in a City Office

Many writers, if they are concerned with the contemporary scene, become involved in murder cases at some point in their lives. As a rule, the involvement is no more than that of the observer. In mid-August 1949, however, I had the unusual experience of knowing the victim of a particularly pointless murder; knowing some of the detectives involved in the hunt for the murderer; knowing the coroner, who later became a friend and whose biography I was to write; and knowing the pathologist, Dr Francis Camps, who conducted the post mortem on the victim.

She was Dorothy Wallis, who dropped her real name Daisy because she did not think it very appropriate for a woman whose life was lived in the busy city atmosphere of High Holborn, London.

Dorothy Wallis, a bright, good-looking thirty-six-year-old spinster with brown, bobbed hair, owned an employment agency in a dingy, ramshackle building not far from the point where New Oxford Street divides itself from High Holborn. A well-known public house, the Three Compasses, whose landlord, Harry Woodcock, has been a friend of mine for many years, is roughly between the junction of the two streets and the building, No. 157, where Dorothy Wallis was murdered. The old Holborn town hall is almost opposite the pub, and the office where I worked as a magazine correspondent when I was not travelling the world was a few yards nearer the murder spot.

The scene has changed so much in twenty odd years that even those who knew the area well now have difficulty in recognizing it. What was once a village, with a recognizable life of its own, whose denizens, both day and night, knew each other, has been 'developed'. Skyscrapers have sprung up all around and the ancient, blackened building where Dorothy Wallis had an office, opposite the famous Moorfields Eye Hospital, has been replaced by a modern clerks' palace.

It was a warm August Tuesday morning, and as I walked to the office I saw a small, battered-looking car pull up on the other side of the road. The sturdy figure of the St Pancras coroner, Sir Bentley Purchase, emerged, gave me a cheery good morning and disappeared into the grim office building, after pointing to his car and obviously giving instructions to the policeman on the door that it must not be moved. He had been summoned from his tiny flat in the Temple about a mile away.

The afternoon papers reported the murder by stabbing of Dorothy Wallis and the following afternoon papers had had time to delve into her background. They came up with very little. Miss Wallis, who was from Willesden in North London, was practically the girl-next-door who, in her mid-thirties, was trying to make good. For years she had been a typist at the Air Ministry, a dead-end job, pleasant enough but boring. She had often talked to friends of escaping from it and had worked out a possible route. In those days, agencies for supplying office staff had not burgeoned as they have now, but Miss Wallis saw the need and was determined to fill it.

Her capital was limited but she found an office at a rent she could afford at the top of No. 157 High Holborn. The exterior of the building was not impressive, but inside it was even worse; gloomy, musty and in some places dust-coated. The shaky stairs that led to the top must have been depressing to most of the girls who went up them looking for jobs. But for Miss Wallis it was a start, and with hard work and luck she believed it would lead to a better future.

Sheila Bennett, one of the young girls who went to the Adelphi Secretarial Agency seeking work, soon found it. Miss Wallis took her on as her own secretary. Miss Bennett subsequently proved to be an observant and useful witness and was able to give the Scotland Yard murder squad, led by Chief Superintendent Harold Hawkyard, much valuable information when they investigated the stabbing of Miss Wallis.

No. 157 High Holborn was not grand enough to employ a commissionaire. Each tenant had a front door key and the first to arrive, as

132

a rule about 9 a.m., opened the door and left it ajar for their own employees and other tenants.

On the morning of the discovery of Miss Wallis's body, Sheila Bennett found the building locked when she arrived just before nine o'clock. That gave her time for a quick coffee at the workmen's café almost next-door. A few minutes later, she was in a state of hysteria. She had climbed the stairs, opened the office door and found Miss Wallis just behind it, on her back. She was covered with blood, and even the inexperienced and frightened girl could see she was dead.

The police arrived immediately afterwards. First came a constable who had been on patrol in the street and was summoned by another tenant of the building after hearing Miss Bennett's screams. Then a divisional detective-inspector and his sergeants arrived from Bow Street, two or three hundred yards away, followed by Chief Superintendent Hawkyard. An elderly couple arrived after the detectives. The man looked through the open door in a bewildered fashion. 'I am Miss Wallis's father,' he said. He had not yet caught sight of the body. 'Dorothy did not come home for supper last night,' he said, apologetically. 'We did not worry at first because we thought she was out with friends. I tried to telephone her this morning when her mother found she had not been home all night but I could get no reply, so my wife and I have come to see what has been happening.'

Camps, arriving soon afterwards, was able to tell them. Miss Wallis, he deduced, had been taken by surprise by her attacker and stabbed in the back, but she had fought desperately for her life. His post mortem on her thin but well-developed body showed two frontal stab wounds which had been made through her dress. 'One stab pierced her heart and there were indications that the knife or dagger used was pushed in again without being completely withdrawn or that she fell forward on it,' he told the inquest. The room showed no signs of a struggle but, said Camps, 'she obviously put up a reasonably good defence. She had clasped the weapon and held up her arms to defend herself.' Camps also said the wounds were severe but she would not have died so quickly that she could not have shouted for help for some seconds.

This is exactly what Miss Wallis had done. Two teenage sisters named Florence Rose and Ethel Crowley, who lived at the back of the building next to No. 157, were able to fix the time of the screams and therefore of the murder. They returned from work to their small flat and after a quick change were almost ready to go out for the evening at 6.30 p.m. when the screams came from the direction of the offices. Ethel, a sixteen-year-old, was either a realist before her time or she had a vivid imagination. She said she had heard the word 'murder' mixed among the screams but did not pay much attention to it. It was a roughish neighbourhood. 'I thought that someone was giving his wife a good hiding,' she said. Connoisseurs of wife-beating would probably say it was a bit too early for that sort of behaviour and when the detectives raised their eyebrows in disbelief she thought up something else. 'It could have been those postmen,' she said. 'We often hear noises and shrieks from the Post Office garage on the corner of Drury Lane.' This was true: in those days shouting and horseplay often overflowed from the W.C.1 postal district garage into the street.

The Adelphi Agency catered for foreign as well as English men and women. As soon as Miss Bennett had recovered sufficiently to be questioned, she was able to give details to the police of the callers at the office on the last afternoon of Miss Wallis's life. There had been a telephonist and a clerk who did not seem to fit into the sinister picture. A young job seeker from North Wembley, Joyce Evelyn Jones, had stayed half an hour while Miss Wallis typed her several introductions to employers. The girl had left the office about ten minutes to six after being reminded that she must let Miss Wallis know if she got one of the positions – Miss Wallis lived on the commission employers had to pay her for finding staff. Miss Jones' impression of the office was not very favourable. She said it was 'very eerie', and that night told her mother she would not go back. 'I had a presentiment that something was about to happen there,' she said later.

Her presentiment was accurate. During the murder enquiries, Miss Iris Wilkins, another of Miss Wallis's clients, came forward to say that she had telephoned Miss Wallis about a job. The smooth voice of an educated man answered and asked what she wanted. She said she wished to speak to Miss Wallis but the man told her she had gone. 'All right,' said the man when Miss Wilkins said she would telephone again, 'but make it earlier next time'

There was some discrepancy in the times witnesses gave of their telephone calls to the Adelphi office, and if matters had gone differently defence counsel would doubtless have made much of it. Joyce said she had left with her letters of introduction at about ten to six, when Sheila Bennett had already gone home. The Crowley sisters swore the murder screams were at 6.30. But Miss Wilkins declared that she had telephoned between five and ten past six, when the man answered after the bell had been ringing for a minute. What was Miss Wallis doing between that time and the time she screamed twenty minutes later?

The man's voice was a mystery. Was he a well-spoken Pole, who according to Miss Bennett, had called at the agency that morning, saying he was desperate for work. Not only had he called but he rang again in the afternoon saying that he had seen a good office that Miss Wallis could rent for £4 a week if she wished. Miss Wallis might have needed a better office but she had not asked the Pole to find her one. She thought the man might be a potential thief, since there were prowlers about and one had stolen a typewriter from her office. If the Pole was not a thief, was he a potential murderer?

Support for the theory that the murder had taken place about the time the Crowley sisters had heard the screams came from two well-known 'villagers', Mr and Mrs Littler, who lived in Bloomsbury Way, north of New Oxford Street. Their 'local' was the Three Compasses which they visited normally about half past six and reached by taking a short cut through a narrow, raised alley called Dunn's Passage, which connects New Oxford Street and High Holborn. The Littlers heard the screams and the sound of a woman sobbing as they walked the short length of the passage. They were just emerging into High Holborn at the other end when a man in his mid-twenties came running into the passage and almost knocked them over in his hurry. He was squarely built and his swarthy face, bushy sideburns and oily black hair gave him the look of an Italian. He had a coat over his arm and had been doing up the sleeves of his sports shirt as he hurried, almost raced towards them. Then he clamped his right hand over his left wrist, as though he was hiding, shielding or holding something. The murder weapon? Or had he received wounds during the fierce struggle with Miss

Wallis, as she tried to defend herself and reach the telephone?

The knife or dagger used was never found and neither was the murderer. Police enquiries lasted many months and a dossier of six hundred statements was compiled. On the day of Miss Wallis's funeral, Arthur Whittington, a young professional photographer, took a panoramic photograph from the roof of the building opposite as the coffin was carried from the Adelphi office to the hearse. Police technicians blew up the photograph and examined it microscopically in the hope that they might recognize the murderer among the morbid sightseers. It was a fruitless exercise.

As Sir Bentley was to say at the inquest, the murder was motiveless. There were obvious suspects – the Pole, the Italian and the man who had answered the telephone, none of whom was traced. But the police knew of the existence of many other suspects, although they were also unknown. For the murdered woman led what almost amounted to a double life. By day she was the demure, efficient seeker of jobs for both sexes. By night she sought out men alone.

In locked drawers at her office, detectives found a number of uninhibited sex books which dealt frankly with the problems arising from the relationship of men and women. Her diaries, entered up in Gregg shorthand, contained the names of many men and cryptic but unmistakable references to her experiences with them. But they were so abbreviated that even the specialist shorthand writers could not make sense of them.

The case puzzled and fascinated both Camps and Bentley Purchase. Bentley Purchase, later in life, could make small jokes about it in appropriate circles. He was introduced to an eminently respectable gentleman who had an office in High Holborn near the scene of the murder. Sir Bentley looked him up and down. 'Yes,' he said, 'same height. Same colour hair. Same build. Opportunity obvious ... I wonder!' The gentleman knew Sir Bentley and laughed, as he walked away humming and shaking his head. Sir Bentley knew, and told me that the police knew, the identity of the killer but the evidence for an arrest was too thin and he was never brought to justice.

A Sister-in-Law is Murdered

Few women can have been as sorely tried or hard-working as forty-six-year-old Mrs Edith Daisy Chubb, of Broadstairs, Kent, who kept house for her husband, her mother and her sister-in-law Miss Chubb, and also looked after her five children. In 1958 she still found time to kill her sister-in-law.

Miss Chubb, a somewhat domineering, middle-aged spinster, worked in the ladies' department of a big store in Cliftonville, Kent, and was set in her habits. Every morning, she left home at 8.40 a.m. and returned after the store had closed at 6 p.m. She seldom went out after that. It was a great surprise when she did not come back from work on 6 February. Nothing could be done that night but the next morning at 10 a.m. Mrs Chubb, in a state, rang the department store and asked whether her sister-in-law had been at work the previous day. The reply was that she had not, and Mrs Chubb went at once to Broadstairs Police Station to report her missing. At 11.15 a.m. that morning, the police went round to Mrs Chubb's house and told her that her sister-in-law was dead. Her body had been found in a hedge not far from where they lived. She was fully dressed in her outdoor clothes and was without her handbag. She had been strangled with a scarf and the doctor called to the body reckoned she had been dead about twenty-four hours.

The finding of the body left Mrs Chubb white and shaken. She made a statement that Lily Chubb had no men friends and she had last seen her alive on the morning of 6 February. The only reason she might occasionally not come home at her regular time was if she went out to tea or to the pictures with a friend. Mrs Chubb described the household as a very happy and united family. 'I just cannot imagine anything like this happening,' she said.

Camps was called in to perform a post mortem and made some surprising discoveries. Miss Chubb had been strangled but there were various marks on her body which Camps said had been made after death. He believed they had been made as a result of Miss Chubb being placed in a chair for some time after she had died. The chair proved to be an invalid chair which the police found in the garden shed. Privately, Camps told the police that the killer might be a woman – which was correct – but that she might have been helped by a man – which was not true.

The police had taken a formal statement from Mrs Chubb and had chatted to her on several occasions about Miss Chubb and her habits, but Camps' discovery of the marks on her body made it necessary for them to go into the affairs of Miss Chubb much more closely. They found that Mrs Chubb seemed to have come into money. She had always lived on the edge of poverty and was in debt before her sister-in-law's death. But after it she began to pay bills, including rent which was owing. 'You have never asked me about money before,' Mrs Chubb complained, when the household budget came under the closest scrutiny. She said her husband gave her £2 a week, she had her mother's pension of £3 and her sister in Ireland had recently sent her £5. As a rule, several people saw Miss Chubb regularly when she left the house to go to work but no one could remember seeing her on the morning of 6 February. 'If she never left the house, it means she must have died indoors,' said Chief Inspector Everitt. Another detective-inspector was with him and Mrs Chubb asked to speak to Mr Everitt alone. 'You are quite right, I killed her,' confessed Mrs Chubb. 'I cannot bear to think about it. But I shall feel better if I tell you. I knew when you saw me on Wednesday that I should have to tell you before long.'

Mrs Chubb then described how, as her sister-in-law Lily was going through the front door, 'something came over me' and she pulled the scarf tightly round Lily's neck. 'She did not struggle. When I realized she was dead I was horror-struck,' her statement said.

The invalid chair was in the garden shed and Mrs Chubb said she had put Lily in it and pushed it back into the shed. It remained there all night and next morning, as soon as her husband had gone to work, she covered Lily with a rug, pushed her in the chair to Reading Street Road, put her on the bank at the side of the road and went home. 'It didn't take me long and I was back indoors by a quarter to six,' added Mrs Chubb. There seemed to be no motive, although Mrs Chubb had taken £12 from her sister-in-law's handbag before she burned it. It must have been obvious to Mrs Chubb, however, that the police would solve the crime in a very short time. Nevertheless, Mrs Chubb insisted that she and her sister-in-law had got on well together and that Miss Chubb had always promised to look after the children if anything happened to her.

The police did arrest Mrs Chubb and, while she was in the care of a woman police officer named Miss Annie Tapp, she was a little more forthcoming than she had been with the men. The motive emerged: a festering hatred of her sister-in-law so deep that it rankled even to see her sit in her husband's chair.

'Nobody knows what I have been through in the last year,' she said. 'Lily was so smug and damned complacent. Nobody knows what she was like. She was self-centred and though she pretended to think so much of the children, I didn't really think it was true. I think she was false underneath. I cannot really say I liked Lilian. I certainly didn't love her. She used to sit in my husband's chair and when he came home, she didn't bother to move.'

Mrs Chubb had a catalogue of woes which could have been listed only by a very tired or disgruntled woman – her husband's bad temper, the neglect by her own family who had never helped her, financially or otherwise, and the fact that Miss Chubb was writing rude letters about her to her sister in Canada, which she saw because she was herself intercepting the returning letters. But what seemed more appalling than anything else was the fact that to make ends meet Mrs Chubb had been working three nights a week, from 8 p.m. to 8 a.m., as a hospital cleaner, although she was a trained nurse.

When Mrs Chubb went into the witness box at her trial, Mr A. P. Marshall, Q.C., asked her whether seeing her sister-in-law sitting about placid and doing nothing had any effect on her. Mrs Chubb agreed it was a little irritating. She said that on 6 February, when her husband had gone to work and the children had been got off to school, the two of them were left alone in the house. She had reached a stage when the smallest things her sister-in-law did upset her. 'I felt irritated at the way she put her cup down,' said Mrs Chubb. 'I followed her downstairs and pulled her scarf. I didn't intend to hurt her. I intended to give her a shake up. She fell backwards on to the floor and struck her head on the post of the stairs.'

At the moment this happened, Mrs Chubb thought she heard the milkman outside. Lilian made a groaning sound and she put her hand over her mouth to stop it. Lilian died. While thinking over what had happened, she made up her mind to leave home. She tidied up the house and paid various bills with money she had taken from Lilian's handbag. Then she changed her mind.

Mrs Chubb's friends stepped forward in her hour of need at her trial. Mrs Evelyn Cook, the matron of Haine Hospital, near Broadstairs, who had known Mrs Chubb since 1936 as an efficient and excellent nurse, said she liked her very much as a person. So did her colleagues and patients, who called her (a nice touch, this) 'the ministering angel of the night'. The matron said she considered Mrs Chubb was a sick woman, in need of a holiday, and the family doctor called her an exceptionally hard worker. But she lived on her nerves, he said, and had never been able to relax. 'Last year, I formed the opinion that she was on the verge of a nervous breakdown,' said Dr Gordon Marshall, 'she felt she was between the devil and the deep blue sea.' He told Mr F. H. Lawton, later Lord Justice Lawton, that he felt that in a moment of stress, and at her time of life, she did something under the impulse of the moment when she could not help herself. She had momentary mental blindness.

But Dr M. K. Williams, Principal Medical Officer at Holloway Prison, who was called for the prosecution to give rebuttal evidence, said he had examined Mrs Chubb on five occasions and found no disease of the mind or nervous illness or mental abnormality.

The jury spent more than two hours debating whether Mrs Chubb was guilty of murder but found she was guilty only of manslaughter, Mr Justice Jones having directed them that they must in any event find her guilty of manslaughter. The judge was not impressed by her story of the incident when she thought she heard the milkman outside and put her hand over Miss Chubb's mouth. 'This woman,' he said, 'is a trained nurse and you may think that the simplest thing in the world would have been for her to deal with the situation and the deceased would have recovered quite quickly ... You must ask yourselves whether the most natural behaviour on the part of a nurse would have been to render some first-aid.'

The sentence was four years' imprisonment and it may be that Mrs Chubb found prison a comparative rest-cure compared with her hard-working life outside prison walls.

Nightmare of a Son-in-Law

Camps was called in 1953 to a sad household in a slummy part of the fashionable district of St Marylebone because an old woman, Mrs Robina Warden-Baird, had been found dead in bed. The woman lived with her daughter, who was mentally defective, and the daughter's husband lived a few doors away but did not see much of his wife or bed-ridden mother-in-law.

On the night of 6 February, the son-in-law had a nightmare which made such a vivid impression on him that he decided there must be something wrong at the house down the street where his wife and mother-in-law lived. As soon as he awoke, and still shaking from his nightmare, he threw on a minimum of clothes and rushed down the street to the house. When his wife opened the door, he knew that his premonition was correct; the strong smell all over the house was the unmistakable smell of death. He rushed past his wife and found his mother-in-law dead in bed.

The woman had died a fortnight earlier, according to Camps' estimate. The unstable daughter knew she was dead, but said pathetically that she was devoted to her mother and had told nobody she had died because she had wanted her to stay with her as long as possible. A small corner of such lives of misery and also of devotion had been exposed for a few minutes. Camps found no evidence of violence and, as he could find no ascertainable cause of death, the coroner accepted that evidence for his verdict.

Murder on the Seventeenth Tee

Murders are not often committed on golf courses, nor, as Sir Richard Jackson, Scotland Yard's late crime commissioner, has pointed out, are they usually the work of people with criminal records. But the attractive golf course to the south of the Hertfordshire town of Potters Bar has been the scene of not one but two shocking murders in recent times. The first of the murderers was never found, although the police believed they knew who he was.

The other provided proof of Sir Richard's contention about the nature of murderers. This man was a young, mild-mannered sadist who worked in the office of the local council.

Camps played no part in events after the first of the murders, which was in 1947. The victim was believed to be a railwayman named Albert Welch, but the police were never quite sure because the body had been hacked to pieces which were then thrown into a dew-pond on the course. There was no apparent motive for the killing but Welch, who lived in a house about a mile from the course, was never seen again after he went out for an evening stroll a few months before.

The other victim was Mrs Elizabeth Rosina Currell, an ordinary middle-aged housewife, who on 29 April 1955 also took her evening stroll on the golf course to exercise her corgi dog. When she had not returned an hour later, her husband was worried. He was even more worried when he heard the dog whimpering and scratching at the front door – without his wife. He knew the route his wife always took and went over it. There was no trace of her. Now thoroughly alarmed, he went to the police and a search was begun by a large party of policemen. Middle-aged ladies do not usually vanish in this way and the policemen, fearing that she had been taken ill or, worse, was the victim of an attacker, continued to scour the course long after it was a practical proposition that they would find her in the darkness. The search was halted about 1.30 a.m. but was resumed at first light. Soon afterwards a policeman found Mrs Currell's body lying by the seventeenth tee. The local police surgeon, Dr David Matthews, needed no more than a glance under Mrs Currell's red coat, which had been thrown over her head, to see that she was dead. He told Detective-Inspector Dennis Hawkins, the policeman in charge, that the body should be examined by a specialist pathologist. 'Send for Professor Camps,' he said.

The body was still lying where it had been found when Camps examined it in the morning. It was as bad a case of murder as he had seen. The motive was clearly sexual and the attacker had made all the preparations. He had ripped off Mrs Currell's knickers and forced her legs apart. Camps discovered later when he did a full post mortem that the murderer must have been interrupted almost in the act because there had not been intercourse. Not only was the skull fractured in four places but the murderer had tried to strangle her with one of her own stockings. Camps said the misused woman had been hit in the face with a fist as well. The cause of death was shock and haemorrhage, plus the attempt at strangulation. The weapon used to murder Mrs Currell was found lying near the body and was the seventeenth tee marker. The $3\frac{1}{2}$ lb piece of metal had been used mercilessly and blood and bits of Mrs Currell's skull were still sticking to it.

Later the murderer told how he had ambushed Mrs Currell from behind. He intended to try to knock her out but she turned round just as he was about to hit her. The two struggled; the older, more sensible woman, who realized what the youth was trying to do, told him not to be silly, but the ordinary-looking youngster did not care what happened to his victim. 'I managed to hit her on the jaw, then I tried to strangle her,' he confessed. 'I thought she was dead and I dragged her over to the hedge where I tried to interfere with her. She was still alive and I had to hit her with the tee iron to kill her. I hit her several times until we were both covered with blood. I remember that while we were struggling she screamed and talked to her little dog which ran away.'

But the murderer still had not done. When he hit Mrs Currell, she fell against the flag post and said she had hurt her back. This did not deter him from making a further attempt to strangle her as she lay on the ground. He then dragged her to the hedge to undress her.

The struggle had been fierce and, in spite of her dreadful wounds, Mrs Currell must have fought like a tigress. Now she could no longer fight back and the attacker was able to rip off her coat, blouse and underclothes. 'She started to come round,' he wrote when he was caught, 'I pulled off one of her stockings and tied it round her neck. It broke straight away and then I hit her with a piece of wood I found underneath the hedge. The wood broke as well, so I hit her with the tee iron. I had to hit her several times before I saw she was dead.'

Not surprisingly after such a terrible struggle – Sir Richard Jackson called it a 'remarkably brutal murder' – the badly injured woman began to bring up a lot of blood and the murderer put her coat over her face to staunch it. 'I wiped my hands on her coat, blouse and knickers. I washed off most of the blood in a stream. I then went home.'

The murder had occurred at the end of April but three and a half months were to pass before the police were able to lay their hands on the man who committed it. Under the direction of Sir Richard at Scotland Yard, well-known senior police officers like Superintendent Leonard Crawford, the Barnet divisional chief, Superintendent Law, Superintendent Salter and Detective-Inspector Dennis Hawkins organized one of the most massive searches ever mounted. It was a combined technical, clerical and above all personal operation. The searchers had little to work on and the obvious motive was not much help. Mrs Currell was a blameless woman, without an enemy, and the detectives reasoned that the crime had probably been committed on the spur of the moment. A young couple walking across the golf course had heard what they thought was a dog yapping and had seen shadowy shapes in the twilight but their thoughts were not on murder and they went on their way.

But the police had a clue on which all hinged. On the tee iron was the tiny part of a right-handed palm-print, not more than an inch across. There was no absolute certainty that the small print belonged to the murderer but if, as Camps said, he had used the tee iron, it was worth while trying to find out whose it was.

Even in those days, the police had built up a collection of six thousand palm-prints at Scotland Yard and, from this collection, the experts under Chief Superintendent Cherrill began to try to match up the tee print. In view of the theory of their chief, they were not altogether surprised when they failed.

While the comparisons were going on, the other obvious but laborious lines of enquiry were proceeding. The co-operation of the chief constables of adjoining counties was sought to question all men with records for assaulting women about their movements on the night of the murder. All submitted to being palm-printed and all were cleared.

The net was thrown overseas but in the police registries as far afield as California and Australia no matching print was found. The police kept a record of the letters they sent out, the house-to-house calls they made, and the palm-prints from men living, working in or visiting the area they had taken and attempted to match. They amounted to more than seven thousand houses visited and 8,889 palm prints taken, figures that might not have been believed if they had not been recorded. The men at headquarters could not keep pace with the palm-prints that poured in and had to be checked. Ordinary police work had to go on, the task of comparing prints was exacting, and the number of officers skilled enough to do it was limited. One moment of inattention could have ruined the entire operation. After a time, to save fatigue and maintain efficiency, the experts were not allowed to work more than every other week at a stretch.

All this produced the murderer. The police had actually interviewed him five days after Mrs Currell was killed, although at the time they did not know it. He was seventeen-year-old Michael Queripel, one of two brothers who lived with their parents not far from the golf course. When detectives had checked at the house, Mrs Queripel had lied, saying that Michael had spent the evening at a local garage with a friend. But of course not all the evening, as the police were to discover.

Queripel agreed to have his print taken on 3 July. It was the 4,605th to be examined and, as soon as it was seen to be a match, a cheer through the department brought officers running from all over the building to congratulate those who had found it. Superintendent Crawford was at his desk in Barnet when they informed him that the print had been matched. 'I knew it would come up in the end,' he exulted.

Crawford and Hawkins needed no instructions to make an arrest. The form on which Queripel's print was recorded contained particulars of his work, and when the detectives arrived at the council offices, they went straight to the treasurer's department. 'Yes, I know what it's all about,' said Queripel, 'I found her. She was dead.' Crawford told Queripel that his palm-print had been found on the tee iron. 'If you found her, why didn't you tell the police?' he asked. Queripel did not answer for some time, but finally he said: 'I hit her, then I tried to strangle her.'

Queripel pleaded guilty at his trial. He made a detailed confession to the police in which he said that the reason he was on the golf course was that he was trying to cure an attack of migraine.

He described the killing and said that when he got home his parents were in bed. Next morning, to explain the blood on his clothes he said he had cut his arm at the garage where he was supposed to have been working on the night of the murder. Actually the wound was small and self-inflicted and could not possibly have accounted for the large amount of blood on his clothes. Queripel stuck to the story he had told his mother – that he had found Mrs Currell dead and had only picked her up to find whether she was alive. But the obvious question remained; why had he not informed the police?

Queripel was not quite eighteen and legally could not have been hanged, but he would probably not have been in any case. Doctors who observed his demeanour said he may not have been sane. Sentence of death was not passed by Mr Justice Hallett, who ordered Queripel to be detained indefinitely.

The major credit for the capture of Queripel, through the identification of his palm-print, must go to the Metropolitan Police officers for their incredible thoroughness. But Camps took some pleasure from the fact that he had pointed out that the tee marker was the murder weapon.

It is interesting to note that this was not the first case in which a conviction had been secured by means of a palm impression. In 1942 a print of a twenty-three-year-old wood machinist named George William Silverosa was found on the butt of a revolver used to batter an old Hackney Road, East London, pawnbroker to death. After three thousand prints had been examined Silverosa and a man named Dashwood were identified. Perhaps the reason why the police were so confident that Queripel would be convicted was that the expert in that, the first case of its kind, was also Superintendent Cherrill.

A Passionate Rumanian

When, in April 1959, a Rumanian workman named Leonie Wendolowsky became friendly with a twenty-six-year-old Brixton girl, Doreen Joan Williams, he was heading for a great deal more trouble than he suspected. He was a scaffolder by trade and had a room in Islington. He entertained Miss Williams as well as his means permitted and in a short time was declaring that he had fallen in love and wanted to marry her. 'I love her more than any other woman in my life,' he told a friend. When he had lived and worked in Bedford, his visits to her were limited to the weekends, but his move to Islington meant that he could see her during the week as well. He had time to find out the sort of girl she really was.

Wendolowsky did not like what he found out. Doreen Williams was a prostitute and she was so deeply involved in the business that she employed a pimp to tout for her. Wendolowsky brooded over the future and fate of the girl, especially when she refused point-blank to give up the life she had chosen to live.

The passionate Rumanian was not the sort of man who should have brooded. He had had mental trouble in the past and a deep scar at the front of his head showed where the surgeon had attempted to relieve the pressure on his brain. His own doctor said that from time to time Wendolowsky had extreme head and gastric pains, could not sleep, and when he did had terrifying nightmares. During a night in late April, Wendolowsky's landlady and landlord heard a commotion in his room but they knew about his nightmares and thought he was suffering from one that was more terrifying than usual. But next morning they forced open the door and found Wendolowsky and Doreen Williams embracing each other – dead.

It was not a suicide pact. Camps reported that Miss Williams had been battered to death with a two-foot-long piece of scaffold tubing loaded with lead and padded on the outside with rags – a murderous weapon when used at close quarters. Wendolowsky had taken a large quantity of the barbiturate, sodium amytal. As the coroner remarked, he had done the job properly.

Wendolowsky had murdered deliberately. He had announced his intention of doing so in a letter to his brother in Baltimore, U.S.A. 'What she was or is, is of no importance but I love her,' wrote the unhappy Rumanian. 'I love her more than any other woman in my life. I have therefore decided to finish her and myself, for always.'

The tragedy for Miss Williams was that in another second she would have escaped with her life. She was found near the door, fully dressed with her hat on, as though she was leaving.

A Fire in Hampstead

Many women murderers have had the appearance of people who, to use a popular phrase, would not hurt a fly. Their method, as a rule, has been poisoning. But in 1954 a tiny, frail-looking, raven-haired woman, with a frame so bent that she might have been carrying all the burdens of her country, was tried in London for a murder which involved violence of two sorts, and fire. She was a Cypriot with the unwieldy name of Styllou Pantopiou Christofi. She was only fifty-three, but with her claw-like hands and once-attractive olive skin turned to wrinkled parchment she looked as old and malevolent as one of Shakespeare's witches.

Though the sun provides some compensation, life is hard for peasants in Cyprus, where lack of water and impoverished land often deny even the best of small farmers an adequate living. Mrs Christofi's husband, when he was active, was not the best of farmers; his olive grove was so small that it scarcely ranked as a grove, and the Christofis and their son, Stavros, were never far from the starvation mark. Poverty, even though she had endured it all her life, made Mrs Christofi a little sourer every year. Like most of the other peasants in the district, she was illiterate and envious of those around her who were better off. The small village in which she lived was her world, and she had little idea what it was like beyond the boundaries. Mrs Christofi did not expect things to be much better, merely a little easier. Her only hope for an improved future was her son Stavros, on whom none of his mother's mean-mindedness had rubbed off. He was good-looking, likeable and go-ahead. He saw there was no future in cultivating an olive grove which would not support even one person adequately and, as soon as he was old enough and could afford a pair of shoes, he walked to Nicosia, the capital, and found a job as a kitchen boy. Nicosia was a thriving city, which was being built up in those days as a tourist centre, but Stavros was looking beyond that. He saved his money, observed how well the waiters did with tips, and, when he had saved his fare and a few pounds over, took a boat for England. On landing, he made for the Cypriot colony in Clerkenwell. He had friends there and it did not take him long to find a job as a wine waiter at the famous Café de Paris in London's West End.

We do not know whether Mrs Christofi eventually undertook the voyage to England on her own initiative or whether it was at the invitation of her son. For twelve years Stavros had had a happy, settled home in Hampstead, but it was a home with a drawback from his mother's point of view. Stavros's wife Hella, a good-tempered German woman of thirty-six, lived there with their three children. Although Hella came from the working class district of Wuppertal, in western industrial Germany, she was sophisticated and used to a good standard of living. She had a good figure and was always faultlessly groomed. Stavros usually worked at nights and, as the children aged eleven, ten and eight needed little looking after during the day, Stavros was willing to stay at home while Hella took a job as a fashion model to provide extra cash.

It was into this contented and happy household that Mrs Christofi insinuated herself and began at once to stir up trouble. She had come from a dark, dirty smelly two-room hovel in Cyprus. Her daughter-in-law's terraced house, near Florence Nightingale's old house, in South Hill Park, Hampstead, was not exactly a mansion but it was comfortable and not overcrowded. Mrs Christofi took an instant dislike to the house and everything in it. Worse, she did not like the way Hella spent Stavros's money, not to say her own, on clothes, lipsticks, creams and other cosmetics, though since she had never seen them before in her life she did not know what to call them. She did not like the way her grandchildren were being brought up and said so, loudly and often.

There were language difficulties, naturally, since the old woman did not speak English and could communicate only with Stavros, in Greek. The peasant woman's resentment at finding things and situations she could not understand flared up every day into torrents of angry abuse which Hella began to dread. On two occasions, Stavros found life for the family so intolerable that he arranged for his mother to live elsewhere. Each time, Mrs Christofi made herself so unpleasant to her hosts that they asked her to return to her son's house. The last time it happened, it was the end of the road as far as Hella was concerned. 'I am taking the children for a holiday to Wuppertal next week and when I come back your mother must go,' she said. The distraught husband asked where his mother must go. 'Back to Cyprus,' was the short, uncompromising reply.

The question never arose because the projected holiday visit to Germany did not take place. Instead, Camps and his friend Bentley Purchase, hurrying to the scene of a fire in Hampstead on the night of 28 July 1954, found a dead woman who was soon identified as Hella Christofi.

Neither Camps nor Purchase was obliged to hasten in the middle of the night to the scene of a crime such as that involving Mrs Christofi, but both took pleasure in being at the centre of events with which they would later be concerned. The police, on Purchase's standing instructions, always telephoned him whenever bodies were found in unusual circumstances; in turn, Purchase telephoned Camps to ask him to come.

Purchase had left the body where it was in the 'area' of the house where Hella lived until Camps' arrival. It was completely unclothed, in a supine position, and seemed to be burned black. The face and hair were covered with blood and there was a 'band' strip all round the neck. When Camps turned the body over, he saw that it was really a mixture of black and white – black where the charring had taken place on the front of the body and white on the buttocks, calves and shoulders which, touching the stone floor, had escaped scorching by the fire.

A superficial view would have been that death was due to burning, deliberate burning, because Camps detected a strong smell of paraffin, which he believed had been poured over the body as it lay on the ground. But Camps never took a superficial view, even at a preliminary examination of a body. He knelt down to take a look at the 'band' area round the neck caused by a ligature and saw that it ran all the way round. The ligature, he thought, might have been a scarf. 'She's been strangled,' he said to Purchase.

But the 'slim, well-nourished, hazel-eyed young woman', to amplify Camps' post mortem report, had not only been burned and strangled; she also had a fractured skull which Camps thought could have been caused by a heavy blow, struck from behind, with the ash plate from the kitchen stove. To support the theory that the attack had taken place in the kitchen, detectives found blotched bloodstains on the wall; some attempts had been made to wash them off.

Preparations for Hella's cremation had been as thorough as her mother-in-law could make them. After carrying or dragging the body out into the 'area' when all was quiet, she piled wood and paper on top of it, sprinkled it liberally with paraffin, and set it alight. This part of her task must have taken up all her attention, because anyone striking a match and using it carelessly near a quantity of such an explosive substance does so at peril.

Mrs Christofi was observed soon after she had set fire to the corpse. Her next-door neighbour, John Young, an engineer, was looking out of his flat window on the first floor while waiting for the last BBC programme for the night to start, when he saw a fire in the area. He thought his neighbours were burning rubbish until he spotted what seemed to be a tailor's dummy in the middle of the fire. It apparently did not cross his mind that the figure might be human. But a wax dummy burning at midnight? Surely an unusual occurrence, even in bohemian Hampstead? Well, the figure looked life-size and, if it was not human, what else could Young think of? As he watched, and waited for the radio programme to come on, he saw the dumpy figure of Mrs Christofi emerge from her door. She bent over the fire to stir up the flames and returned to the house, apparently satisfied with the way the fire was going.

It would have been for psychiatrists to determine whether the old Cypriot woman, with her low-grade mentality, had ever thought out the logical conclusion of her actions. She may have struck her daughter-in-law on the head deliberately and then strangled her in cold blood – she had cut the scarf she had tied round Hella's neck and put parts of it in the dustbin – but how could she hope to dispose of the body. A body is not particularly combustible material and most people, including the ignorant, know that crematoria work at extremely high temperatures. A few sticks of wood and bits of paper, even when soaked with paraffin, would hardly generate enough heat in the open air to completely destroy a body.

We do not know whether the murderess had made any prior, conscious effort to solve the problem of disposing of the body or whether she was even more ignorant than she seemed. But an hour after she had lighted the fire, the body was still there, although charred. Was it panic that made Mrs Christofi decide to call someone else to the scene? She certainly ran out into the main road, stopped a passing car, and told the driver, a Mr Burstoff, in broken English, that there had been a fire. 'Please come. Fire burning. Children sleeping.' Mr Burstoff, a restaurant manager on his way home from work at that late hour, jumped out of his car and, with his wife, followed Mrs Christofi to the still-burning body.

The Hampstead police were soon attracted by the noise from spectators and the acrid smoke from the body. Pertinent and serious questions were asked. The son, Stavros, was brought from his work and interpreted police questions for his mother, who seemed remarkably calm amidst all the extraordinary activity around her. She explained, as though it was something quite out of the ordinary, that every evening, no matter how late, Hella always stripped herself in the kitchen and thoroughly washed her body in a bowl of water.

Mrs Christofi said she had gone to bed late that evening. 'Before I went to bed, Hella said she was going to do some washing,' said her mother-in-law. 'I got up at one o'clock and saw smoke. I opened the bedroom door and at the top of the stairs I saw that the street door was open. I went straight to Hella's room to call her. I got no reply and saw that she was not in bed.' Mrs Christofi said she went downstairs and found the kitchen door was open and the lights on. 'I went across the kitchen to the yard,' she recalled, 'I saw Hella lying on the floor with her head near the door and her arms raised.' She saw little flames at her ankles, round the knees, and at the back of the head. Her face was covered with blood. Mrs Christofi said she splashed water over her. 'It seemed I could do nothing and I ran for help.' But there was something she did before running for help. She removed Hella's wedding ring and later hid it behind a vase in the room.

If Mrs Christofi had not committed the murder, who had? And why did the whole area smell so strongly of paraffin if it had not been used to light the fire to burn up Hella's body? Mrs Christofi had a ready, if fatuous answer. She said there had been two men around the place carrying a suitcase, who might have done it. As for the strong smell of paraffin, she told Detective-Superintendent Leonard Crawford, who charged her with murder, that some days previously she had spilt paraffin on the floor and had stepped on it, possibly causing the smell.

Mrs Christofi made her mark on the statement to the police when it had been interpreted to her by Stavros, and she was taken into custody. It was just over a year since she had arrived in England. Three months later, an Old Bailey jury found her guilty of the murder of her daughter-in-law. There was some evidence on which she might have been judged insane but she would not be deflected from her plea of not guilty. In Britain women murderers, except poisoners, are usually treated more sympathetically than men, but there was no reason why any sympathy should have been extended to Mrs Styllou Pantopiou Christofi. Many years before, in Cyprus, she had been charged, together with two other village women, with the murder of another woman. It was a murder that also involved fire. The two other women had held open the victim's mouth while Mrs Christofi thrust a burning torch down her throat. For some reason, Mrs Christofi was acquitted of that murder. This time she was hanged.

Two Girls

Camps played his part in the hunt for the murderer of Ann Noblett, a seventeen-year-old student of Wheathampstead, Herts, by performing the post mortem after she had been found dead in a wood at the end of December 1958 at Whitwell, six miles from her home. He thought at first that there might be complicated causes of death but came to the conclusion that it was caused by asphyxia due to compression on the neck. This, he told the coroner, did not necessarily mean strangulation. The girl had been interfered with sexually.

Two thousand people were interviewed by the police about her death but no clues emerged. The girl was home-loving, of good character, and had no known boyfriends. Her father said that when she went out he always knew where she was going. The police combed almost the whole of rural Hertfordshire before the body was found, a month after she had disappeared. Camps believed the body had probably been kept in a refrigerator to foil attempts to find out the exact time of death. The verdict at the Hitchin inquest was murder by somebody unknown.

Whenever there is a big murder hunt, the police are pestered by mischievous and malicious telephone calls which often waste hundreds of hours of police time. One man, Walter Edward Nunn, a material handler, of Luton, was responsible for thirty-five such telephone calls during the investigation of Ann's death. He rang the police seventeen times with misleading information and the remaining eighteen calls were to people connected with the investigation. When he was caught, Nunn admitted that he had made the calls out of spite against the police for interviewing him in connection with the murder. Nunn was an unstable character who had had hysterical fits in the past. He had been sent to Borstal for putting poison in his brother's coffee, fortunately without fatal results. His punishment for this stupid crime was six months imprisonment.

The Essex police went to even greater lengths to find the murderer of a Dutch girl, Mary Krick, two years older than Ann Noblett, who was found dead in a ditch a few weeks before Ann's death. Camps said Miss Krick's wounds were inflicted by a blunt weapon which the police did not find, although two hundred policemen searched local roads and by-ways with mine detectors in the hope of doing so. In the course of enquiries, the Essex CID interviewed twenty thousand people, took hundreds of statements, and checked five thousand vehicles and their occupants. Regretfully they closed the case, but no one could say they had lacked persistence.

The Child Who Saw a Murder

London had become a city with an unenviable reputation for violence in the late forties but it was not usual, even then, for the police to come across two battered bodies on the same day and in the same place. This happened in August 1949 when Chief-Inspector John Jamieson, head of 'D' Division's CID, was leading a search for a missing three-year-old child with blue eyes and curly hair named Marion Ward, who lived in Adelaide Road, St John's Wood, North London. Before Jamieson found little Marion's body lying in the neglected grounds of a twenty-room blitzed Georgian mansion, he stumbled across that of a man which had been so disfigured by the weather that it was hardly recognized as a body until the severed head was found nearby. The body was so badly decomposed that at first the police thought it must have lain in the open for a long time, but they changed their minds when they found underneath it a newspaper dated 29 June 1949. It had taken just under six weeks to reduce it to such a state that all Camps could do was to estimate that the man's height had been about six feet and that the cause of death was unascertainable.

Superintendent F. R. Cherrill later took finger-prints and, because the man had a criminal record, the body was established as being that of Reginald Short. He was not only homeless but apparently friendless, and no one came forward to claim his acquaintance or body.

Little Marion Ward had a comfortable home and was greatly loved by her parents, a glue factory manager and his wife. When Marion did not return after playing with her small friends on the afternoon of 12 August, the distraught parents began to search the streets themselves before calling in the police, who had no illusions about what might have happened. A systematic search of the many bombed houses in Avenue Road was organized and in a ground floor room of the derelict Langham Court the body of Marion was found, her blood mingled with the dust that had accumulated over the years.

Camps was rushed to the scene and examined the child's almost pulped head. He counted nine separate blows to the head, several fractured ribs, and other injuries, caused with a blunt instrument. He gave the cause of death as shock and haemorrhage, due to brain injuries, following a fracture of the skull.

Who could have inflicted such terrible injuries on an innocent child? The police knew they were looking for a maniac and it was imperative to discover quickly whether the murderer was a neighbour or perhaps a tramp lurking in the bombed house.

No one in the neighbourhood had seen a tramp or anybody else acting suspiciously, but the police soon became aware that James Tierney and his wife, Nora Patricia, merited the closest investigation. They were a quarrelsome Irish couple – she was 'from the bogs', said her own counsel, Mr James Burge – and neighbours told of noisy scenes when Mrs Tierney's Irish blood was up. Tierney admitted that he was afraid of his wife and said she had once attacked him with a knife. Mrs Tierney, a good-looking woman with a soft voice, denied it and said her husband was always the aggressor. Wherever the truth lay, Tierney decided he had had enough in the days before Marion died and, although he had no job and nowhere to go, he left his unhappy household. Mrs Tierney was later to say that he had done this before, which confirmed, if true, that the quarrels between the two were devastating.

One of the first children to whom Chief-Inspector Jamieson spoke was the Tierneys' six-year-old daughter, Stephanie. She was one of the party of playing children on the afternoon Marion died, and the guileless child told him a story which sent him straight indoors to see Mrs Tierney. Whether Mrs Tierney was aware of any of the standard police procedures in murder cases was never revealed, but when she was asked whether police forensic scientists could take scrapings from under her finger nails and threads from her cardigan, her sense of the danger caused her to blurt out what was obviously a prepared story. She said she had not killed the little girl. 'I will tell the truth about what happened. I didn't do it. My husband did it. I can show you the clothes he was wearing,' she said. Jamieson asked her what her husband had used to kill Marion. 'A hammer,' she said, and offered to show him where it was.

A strange, almost nonsensical story, which involved the name of Haigh, the acid-bath murderer, was the immediate cause of Tierney walking out, according to Mrs Tierney. While she was getting the Sunday dinner ready, he was reading about Haigh in the *News of the World*, and did not seem at all interested in what he was going to eat. Suddenly he looked up and remarked: 'If I had to do a murder, could you tell me which would be the best way to do it without being caught?' 'No,' replied Mrs Tierney. 'Such things never enter my head.'

Tierney snapped back at her. 'No, such things never enter your head! All you think about is what Jamie will look like when he is a man.' Jamie was the baby son of the marriage. Before Tierney walked out, he was said to have made a final remark as cryptic as the rest of the conversation. 'Last night, I was dreaming about crosses,' he said. 'I am beginning to think one can look like Haigh.'

That was on 8 August. There was a difference of opinion about the date on which Tierney returned home, and Mrs Tierney obviously appreciated how important it was that her story should be believed. She said he had come back on 12 August, the date on which Marion was murdered. Tierney insisted that it had been 13 August. On that date, Mrs Tierney said, her electric iron went wrong and, as she knew her husband was around, she went to look for him. Stephanie and Marion were playing outside and she let them go with her. 'I decided to look in on Langham Court. The children ran into the room on the right. It was a big room and when I entered the room, my husband was hitting Marion round the face and head with a hammer. He told me to get out. I tried to grab Marion but he threw me to the ground and I ran out frightened.'

From the jury's point of view, the fatal flaw in the story was that if the police believed it Mrs Tierney would have told it from the witness box and her husband would have been in the dock. But the police did not believe it and one fact that convinced them she was lying was that her footprints, not Tierney's, were found in the dust at Langham Court.

Tierney went into the box to speak of his unhappy married life both in Ireland and London. He said that during his time away from home he was 'sleeping rough' and never went near Langham Court. But when he returned, he and his wife had a conversation about Marion's murderer. His wife asked him what would happen to the murderer, if caught. Tierney told her he would be tried and have to stand the consequences. His wife became hysterical and said, 'It was I who done it.' He asked her why and she said she did not know. 'I didn't believe her,' said Tierney. 'She then described how she had hit the child over the head with a hammer.'

The police already had the hammer, which they had found under a pile of stones in a nearby park. Again, husband and wife told completely different stories of how it came to be there. Mrs Tierney's account was that, during the discussion about the murder, Tierney asked her to confess because 'they will hang a man but not a woman for such a crime'. They were in the park and Tierney had dug a hole in which to hide the hammer. After wiping the handle he gave it to her to put into the hole, remarking, 'You will have to confess now your finger-prints are on the handle.'

Mr Justice Hilbery and the jury did not hear in court the real reason why the police believed Tierney and not his wife, but I discovered it when, in order to write his biography, I was reading the papers of Sir Bentley Purchase, the St Pancras, London coroner who held the inquest on Marion Ward after Mrs Tierney's trial.

There had been an eye-witness of the killing – six-year-old Stephanie, Mrs Tierney's daughter. Unknown to Mrs Tierney, the child had given Chief-Inspector Jamieson a full account of the dreadful deed and Sir Bentley included it in his report, although he did not refer to it in public. Stephanie had told Jamieson that her mother had killed Marion. There had been a small struggle when Mrs Tierney pulled a handkerchief round Marion's mouth. Marion tried to get it off and called out for her own mother. 'My Mummy took a hammer out of a brown handbag,' said Stephanie, 'then Mummy took the handkerchief off Marion's mouth. Marion fell down and Mummy kept hitting her on the head. Marion's eyes were still open and Mummy said "She is not dead yet. She is hard to kill." '

Many students of crime must have wondered why Stephanie was not called to give evidence at her mother's trial. Were the prosecution confident that Mrs Tierney's story was so preposterous that she would convict herself when she gave it as evidence? The question was finally settled by Mr Henry Elam, one of the team which prosecuted Mrs Tierney, who later told the Medico-Legal Society. He said that Mrs Tierney was mad by the legal yardstick of the M'Naghten rules, but she would not allow that defence to be run. Here was a mother murdering a very young child in the presence of her own offspring but running the defence that 'I didn't do it at all'.

'The question arose,' said Mr Elam, 'whether we should call the young child to say "Yes, Mummy did it. I saw it happen." I exercised my discretion and did not call the young child because it would have had the effect of stamping on her mind something that she most probably, indeed certainly, wanted to forget.' Mr Elam said the jury were out some time, during which the police officer in charge of the case came up and said, 'You see, Mr Elam, you would not call the child.' But at that moment, the jury came back and found her guilty. 'It was an exercise in discretion that came off,' said Mr Elam.

It came off, but Mrs Tierney, mad though she was, had had her own story ready in case the prosecution called the child. 'My husband has been telling Stephanie all the week not to tell anybody that he did it. He promised to buy her a new coat if she said nothing.'

It was a sad and pointless crime, without motive. The jury of three women and nine men decided that Mrs Tierney was guilty but insane and Mr Justice Hilbery sent her to Broadmoor.

Edwina Taylor's Death

Within a very short time of the finding of the body of four-year-old Edwina Taylor in the cellar of a house in Upper Norwood, South-east London, the police knew who the killer was, but they did not know where to find him. Edwina was a pretty child, and when she vanished on the afternoon of 31 August 1957 the Metropolitan Police, under Detective-Chief Superintendent John Capstick, mounted one of the biggest 'manhunts' in its history. The little girl's face became one of the best-known in Britain. It was flashed on cinema screens and television sets, printed on posters and in the newspapers. Yet such a massive coverage of her disappearance produced nothing; it could never have produced any sort of result because before the campaign had started the little girl was dead.

When a child disappears from home, every crank in Britain seems to contact the police with suggestions and 'sightings' of the child. The police never dare to ignore the slightest hint of a clue, however ludicrous, in case it may be the one they are seeking.

As soon as Edwina Taylor disappeared, the police asked two lorry drivers, whose descriptions were given, to come forward, because one of them was reported to have given a middle-aged woman and a child like Edwina a lift to the west country. There were no lorry drivers of that sort. Shortly afterwards, a woman and a child of the same description were said to have boarded a Paddington train for Paignton, Devon. Anxious to help to trace the couple, cinema owners in Devon flashed pictures of the child on their screens, requesting information of both woman and child. Nearer home, Capstick called local south-east London newspaper editors to his office and asked them to print appeals to householders to search their cellars, attics, lumber rooms and sheds in the hope of finding the missing child.

Little Edwina was not the only person missing in the district. A man named Derrick Edwardson, a thirty-one-year-old factory labourer, had left his ground floor flat about the same time that Edwina had disappeared. There had been reports that, late the previous night, two cars had arrived noisily and left quickly. The police decided that they were not connected with the girl's disappearance. But they did express an urgent desire to see Edwardson. They knew that he had a criminal record, was unstable, and had previously indecently assaulted one little girl and threatened to murder another.

At 4 p.m. on 9 September, after the daily dawn to dusk hunt, the child's body was found by two police aides – men who normally wear uniform but were working in plain clothes on this occasion. It was in a cellar a quarter of a mile from Edwina's home and it was at Edwardson's house.

Camps, accompanied by Dr Haler, arrived at the house during the early evening and saw the child's body lying on a mound of coal, fully clothed except for knickers, and strangled. At the full post mortem later in the evening, Camps found she had been sexually assaulted and hit hard on the head and face with a heavy weapon.

To a large extent, the police had to rely on Edwardson's own statements and on material found at his flat to supplement Camps' findings. There was blood of Edwina's group in his kitchen and on his suit. The hairs of a dog on the child's shoes came from his dog and fibres from her coat were found in the turn-ups of his trousers.

His description of his crime was chilling. He said he had enticed Edwina to his flat and strangled her with the intention of raping her after death – a refined form of necrophilia, according to a psychiatrist. 'I realized I had killed someone somebody must have loved and I felt ashamed of myself,' he said. 'I pushed her into the coal cellar. Later, I could not get the smell of the decaying body out of my mind.'

Edwardson, probably not realizing that Camps had carried out a post mortem, said he had not interfered with the child, which was untrue. He said he had not gone to work on the morning of the murder but had bought an axe to use for chopping firewood. He had used a usual ploy with such degenerates; he had enticed the little girl to his flat by giving her sweets. The child said her dinner was nearly ready, but he took her to the flat just the same, 'not with the intention of killing, just to assault her and take her home again'.

Edwardson said he had knocked Edwina unconscious with the blunt end of the axe. He tried to revive her but seems to have done it in a peculiar way. He gripped her by the throat and then realized that he had strangled her. But the thought of the face of the strangled child seems to have haunted him in the days that followed. He told the police he had got up in the middle of the night to look at her in the cellar. 'It made my hair stand on end, although I only looked at her feet,' he muttered.

At Gipsy Hill Police Station he told detectives that he supposed he would hang for his crime. 'It has been like a nightmare since it happened,' he said. 'I won't have to see the child again, will I?' Edwardson did not have to see his little victim again. He was found guilty and sentenced to life imprisonment in a secluded world where little children are in no danger; they are not allowed in prisons.

The 'Baby Farm' at Harwich

'Baby-farming' has been an outmoded occupation in Britain for many generations but a case which came perilously close to it occurred in the summer of 1953 at Harwich. It was not on a large scale – only five new-born babies were involved. It started as a simple concealment of the birth of one baby, of which the law, quite correctly, takes a severe view, but the dead baby was presently joined by others. Discovery was not inevitable and it might never have happened but for what might be termed an accident, followed by an act of God. The winter floods which caused such havoc around Harwich and elsewhere in coastal districts that year were followed by a dismal harvest – of dead infants!

The accident which was the start of it all occurred to Mrs Alice Jessie Elsey, wife of a sailor, at a time when he was at sea during 1938. Mrs Elsey was living with her mother, who had her own four children with her, in Mrs Elsey's small house in Vansittart Street. Mrs Elsey became pregnant and, while admittedly some women show few signs of pregnancy, it seems a little strange that neither her own mother, living at such close quarters, nor the neighbours should have noticed it. The circumstances under which the baby was born were stranger still. It came in the middle of the night, in the sitting room, and without the help of doctor or midwife. The baby was dead when it was born and next day Mrs Elsey climbed the short step-ladder on the landing to the attic and put the baby there.

This baby, nameless and a skeleton when eventually it was taken with the four others to Camps' post mortem room, was the last of the batch he examined. Camps put this child aside with the others, which were also skeletons, and concentrated on the last two babies to be assembled, which had the only soft parts still in a recognizable state. The soft flesh indicated to Camps that these two babies had died most recently.

The bones and a single finger-nail had been found on 25 June, under a pile of old clothes, by two electricians who were re-wiring the house at Harwich and making it habitable after the January floods. The skeletons were little more than heaps of small bones but they were augmented two days later by other bones and what Camps called 'material obtained from sweeping the floor'.

Camps was well aware when he first inspected the little piles of bones at Harwich that he had a testing reconstruction task ahead of him. Mice had been busy in the attic and such flesh as there was left on the babies was dry, and in some cases extremely desiccated. Camps, drawing on his vast knowledge, knew fairly quickly that he had the major parts of the skeletons of five infants to assemble. Little more than a glance showed that two of the babies were larger and probably older than the others and his final report, based to a large extent on the lengths of such bones as the femurs, humeri, tibias and radia, supported his opinion that the last two babies to die had gone to between nine and ten months, the next two were eight to nine months, and the first to die was aged only eight months. Camps made his last finding because of the absence of all soft parts and many skull bones.

Camps could not tell from his preliminary examination what sex the skeletons had been or how they had died. But he made progress after soaking the bodies in water. He found that two of the babies retained the remains of uteri and were therefore female. The sex of the other three was uncertain, although evidence of the length of a bone of the greater sciatic notch, measured with an epidiascope, suggested that one skeleton might be male.

The pathologist thought he had gathered together all the bones from the 'baby farm' in Harwich but it was soon uncertain whether he had done so because he could not complete the skeletons. But another parcel from the Harwich police, containing more 'sweepings', helped to fill in the picture. A third parcel of 'sweepings' was needed to supply the remaining few missing bones from the skeletons. There had been talk in the town that a sixth skeleton might be found but it was groundless.

In his final report, Camps said he could tell the approximate order in which the infants had died, from examining the degree of destruction of the soft parts, the amount of skin left adhering to the skull, and the skull's general condition. There was no evidence of violence or injury to the babies but he could neither say what was the cause of death nor whether they had been alive at birth.

While Camps had been doing his post mortems, the Harwich police were not idle. It was an extraordinary state of affairs to have accidentally found the skeletons of five children in an attic and the police had to try to get an explanation for it. Mrs Elsey was the one person who could help them but the story she had to tell was confused and contradictory. She had lived with her sad secret for a long time, sharing it with no one, not even her husband – 'I tried to forget them but never succeeded,' said the apparently placid, ordinary housewife. But when the secret was drawn into the light, she seemed unprepared for the interrogation that was bound to follow. Perhaps a clue to her bewildered, ostrich-like attitude was her remark that she never thought anyone would ever go into the attic.

Mrs Elsey, when questioned by Detective-Sergeant Bond prefaced her remarks with a phrase that hardly ever meant what it said: 'I will be honest with you.' At first, she was not. She said there were only two dead babies originally in the attic and they were her own. She denied vehemently that she had taken the babies' lives and said they were born dead, and she had put them where they were found about ten years ago. Detective-Sergeant Bond, plainly nonplussed that she had put only two babies in a place where five were found, asked about the other three. 'If you say there were five, there must have been but I don't remember having them,' said Mrs Elsey.

Mrs Elsey was well-known in the town and Detective-Sergeant Bond had made a check on the number of children she had had while she had lived there. On her own calculations, he came up with the surprising number of twelve – three known to have been born dead, four who were alive, plus the five in the attic, which she said were hers. 'It does not sound true,' said the detective.

It was not true and the sceptical head-shaking of the detective convinced Mrs Elsey that it was time to tell the truth. 'They're not all mine,' Mrs Elsey admitted, 'but nobody else in the family knows about them. I am to blame and I will take the blame.'

It had all happened a long time ago. The first baby had come as a surprise because she had never seen a baby born before. She said she thought her husband was the father. But she did not tell him that she was going to have a child and as he was often away at sea he had not noticed that a baby was on the way. Life had been difficult for a woman on her own during the war and she found it was pleasant to go into public houses at night for a drink and to 'enjoy herself'. Her second baby was born and disposed of with as little fuss as the first.

It is not quite clear how a woman named Grace Probert came on the scene at this stage, or how she left it. If Grace Probert ever existed, the likelihood is that the women met while drinking in the Harwich pubs. After a few drinks, they probably began to tell each other of their troubles. According to Mrs Elsey's story, Grace Probert said she lived with a sailor at Shotley when he was ashore but had a room at Ipswich. Though Mrs Elsey never went there, she had invited Mrs Probert to her own room, but the visit was not a success. Mrs Elsey's mother said the woman was loose and advised her against continuing the friendship. But by this time the women were deep in each other's confidence and found a most extraordinary coincidence to share. Mrs Elsey told her new friend in strict confidence that she had two dead babies in the attic. For her part, Mrs Probert disclosed tremulously that she had *two* – yes, *two* – dead babies also and did not know what to do with them. It is difficult to imagine the scene and the conversation between two apparently normal women. But had the exchanges of confidence really taken place between Mrs Elsey and Mrs Probert – if Mrs Probert existed – or did they simply exist in the mind of Mrs Elsey?

One fact was beyond dispute. Mrs Elsey's babies were already in the attic and those of Mrs Probert – again, if they were her babies – were soon to join them. Mrs Elsey was even considerate enough to lend Mrs Probert an attaché case in which she could bring her babies from Ipswich and 'hide them up' in her own attic. And that was not quite the end of the story. Six months later – we do not know whether the women were still meeting regularly at the time – Mrs Probert asked for the loan of the case again. 'I will bring something down in it,' she said, as if she was doing her friend a favour. The subject of money was never mentioned. The attaché case duly reappeared two or three weeks later in a public house and Mrs Elsey later found inside a parcel she knew contained a baby. 'I hid it in the roof,' said Mrs Elsey. The baby, like the others, she said, had been still-born.

There was no mention either of Mrs Probert or of any other woman who might have been involved in the baby-farming activities at Harwich, when the case was heard at Essex Quarter Sessions. The skeletons in the attic were certainly not a figment of Camps' imagination but, apart from some police doubts about the number of babies involved, no evidence was brought that all the children had been Mrs Elsey's.

Prosecuting counsel, Mr R. J. Lowry, said everything he could in Mrs Elsey's favour. There was no suggestion that the babies had died in any other way than she had explained. Her character was good and she and her husband had now made up their differences. She had steadied up, drank little and while awaiting trial had been happy, except for the shadow hanging over her head. She nodded as counsel said she was profoundly grateful that her

165

husband was prepared to stand by her and see her through her troubles, so that she might settle down again to lead a normal, sensible life.

But that was not to be, for some time at least. Five skeletons in a cupboard were too many to be overlooked. The chairman of the Sessions, Mr S. G. Turner, Q.C., said the Bench found it impossible to think of a worse case of concealment of birth. There might be some reasonable explanation regarding her own children, if what Mrs Elsey said was true. 'But,' said Mr Turner, 'as to the children of the other woman or women, it really looks as if something in the nature of a traffic was going on.' The wardresses led Mrs Elsey off in tears to serve two years on each of four charges, but the sentences were to run concurrently.

The Girl Who Disappeared

Camps was called by his friend Bentley Purchase in August 1951 to a house in Highbury Hill, North London, to examine what was at first believed by neighbours to be a large yellow doll but which he soon identified as the body of a girl between two and a half and three years old. He thought the child might have been dead for about ten years and what first made him suspect that it was not a natural death was that in the mortuary he found the tiny skull had been fractured in two places. Detectives came but there was not much more help Camps could give them because he was not able to say if the fractures had been caused before or after death, or with what sort of instrument. But he did think, as far as he could see, that the girl had been well looked after while she was alive.

The child was Muriel, the young daughter of Mr and Mrs Ernest Makinson, and the body was found in a curious and casual fashion. Her sixteen-year-old sister Ann found her in a sack on the top of a cupboard as she was putting her brothers' football away one evening. Ann was the eldest of the original Makinson tribe of eleven, of whom sister Mary and brother Joseph had died and little Muriel had quite unaccountably disappeared. In such a big family, Ann assumed many of the duties of a 'little mother' and it was one morning, about eight years before, that she noticed Muriel was no longer with them. The dazed sister had wandered about looking for Muriel. It was true that the Makinson household was by no means conventional, apart from its size. People did disappear – her father, for instance. He had left the house one morning and had not come back for nearly twelve months, and only in a roundabout way did Ann discover that he had been in prison. She tackled her short-tempered mother, Maude. 'What's happened to Muriel?' she said. Her mother told her sharply to mind her own business and said if she heard any more questions of that sort there would be trouble.

When Ernest Makinson came out of prison and asked the same question, he received the same dusty answer and he was in no position to argue with her, either. 'If you start asking questions like that,' she said, 'I shall disappear as well.'

In that part of Highbury where the Makinsons lived, neighbours generally mind their own business, but the news of the discovery of a 'doll' in a sack caused one of them to have a word with a friendly policeman. A senior detective followed to ask whether the Makinsons had known what was in the sack. 'I didn't know it was there,' Mrs Makinson replied. Her husband echoed: 'I have never seen it before.'

After two false starts, Mrs Makinson made a statement which Detective-Inspector Rawlings accepted as true. She said Muriel had been naughty, and when she slapped the child she had struck her head on a gas stove. Next morning, she took up some milk to the child and found her in a sort of fit. Her face went mauve and she died. 'I just panicked,' said Mrs Makinson, 'I thought I would keep the body. I didn't put it in the sack for several weeks. I put it in a chest of drawers with a nightdress on.' There apparently, it remained.

When the blitz started, the family was evacuated to Rotherham in Yorkshire. Mrs Makinson left the body behind in a sack and at some point later she told her husband that Muriel had died. Their Islington home in Treaty Street had been broken into when they returned in 1946 and Mrs Makinson said the sack containing the body had been put by the burglars in the cellar.

Camps had found burns on the body and Mrs Makinson admitted

167

that she had tried to destroy it in the household fire but it would not burn. There seemed to be a possible case of murder or manslaughter against Mrs Makinson, largely due to her own lack of straightforwardness. Camps' fairness in presenting his findings – two fractures of the skull and evidence of burning are not easy to explain away, especially when the body has been concealed – went a long way to bolster up Mrs Makinson's story. Camps gave the cause of death as unascertainable, Sir Bentley Purchase, the coroner, did not dispute the facts, and the Director of Public Prosecutions, the final authority, decided to let the matter drop.

'Here is an Announcement ...'

No murderer on the run has ever been more fully described or had his photograph circulated more widely than William Pettit, a twenty-seven-year-old labourer of Eltham, London, whom the police sought for nearly three weeks late in 1953. Pettit earned this dubious distinction because, apart from the massive coverage in the newspapers, and on the cinema screens, he was the first wanted man to have his photograph sent out by television.

Camps was called to a field in Chislehurst, Kent, in mid-September 1953 to see the body of Pettit's victim, a woman with knife wounds. He had no difficulty in giving the cause of death. A vicious, single, savage blow with a dagger had pierced her heart, causing death from shock and haemorrhage. The dagger was inscribed 'I cut my way', and the murderer had used it to do exactly that.

There was no difficulty, either, in naming the murderer. He was William Pettit, a former lodger at the home of civil servant, A. J. Brown, and his wife, Rene Agnes, at Plassey Place, Eltham. The reason for the crime was also obvious. Pettit imagined he was in love with Mrs Brown, who was almost old enough to be his mother. He was making a nuisance of himself and had been told to go. After the opening of the inquest, Mr Brown proclaimed that he knew who had done it. The only difficulty was to find the man and get him in custody before he could do it again. Mr Brown announced that he was consulting a medium immediately to find out

Pettit's whereabouts. The medium was a failure.

The decision to screen the photograph of the wanted man on television was not made lightly. Many people believed that it would create an awkward precedent and cause legal complications. The same question had been raised when suggestions were first made that the 'media', as it is now called, should be used to catch wanted people. The problem bristled with difficulties but the authorities finally made the decision to screen. The matter of presentation was also thrashed out. The charming Sylvia Peters was the duty announcer but it was felt that a woman was not quite suitable to make such a serious announcement and John Snagge was called in.

The photograph was not much in itself – it was shown in profile and full face – but the description that went with it was more than adequate. Pettit, it said, was five feet ten inches tall, with a sallow complexion and dark-brown, bushy hair. He had brown eyes, sunken cheeks and a slight cleft chin and he walked with a stoop and slightly swinging gait. His tweed overcoat was green and he wore a sports jacket and trousers.

The transmission of the photograph was sandwiched between a news-reel and a show from the headquarters of the Magic Circle and the results certainly caught the attention both of those who were listening to the news and of those who believed in magic. The response was staggering. There were several hundred telephone calls, each saying they had seen the missing man, and the 'brains' at the Lime Grove studios did more than merely log them. They plotted a course they believed the man was taking, using as a guide the places from which the heaviest concentrations of telephone calls came. Pettit was 'sighted' by the largest number of people in the London area but he was believed to have gone north via the Great North Road and eventually was reported to have been seen in Manchester. Needless to say, Interpol and the French police were specially alerted.

After a time, the hue and cry died down. The police still kept a close watch for Pettit in the Eltham area because it was thought that he might try to injure Mr Brown. Until he killed Mrs Brown, Pettit had apparently not kept up a grudge against her, because a couple as incongruous as Mrs Brown and Pettit had been observed having a meal at a Farnborough restaurant. Mrs Brown, a skilled musician, had 'obliged' with a Chopin nocturne. It was the day before her death.

Pettit had been violent previously and had a few convictions for petty crime. When Mr Brown warned him to keep away from his wife, Pettit had retaliated by breaking a window of his house. The police gave him a further warning, after he had spoken of stabbing Mrs Brown.

Pettit was found at last in one of the places the police would never have thought of searching – a bombed building in Budge Row, Cannon Street, a busy thoroughfare in the City of London. He was dead. There was no doubt it was Pettit; his identity card, birth certificate, clothing coupons and other documents were found in his pockets. On a dirty piece of notepaper, which was all he had, he wrote a last note to Mr Brown: 'Forgive me for what I have done. I could have gone on living with Mr and Mrs Brown but not without Mrs Brown. I love her, I love her, I love her.'

Professor Keith Simpson, and not Camps in this case, did the post mortem. He found that Pettit had advanced tuberculosis and, while his death could not be attributed to any particular cause, it was probably natural. Simpson estimated the death had taken place four to six weeks previously but a small clue found near the body gave a more exact date. It was a newspaper on which Pettit had been lying.

The date it bore was presumably the day before Pettit died and it showed that when the nation-wide hunt for him was launched Pettit was already dead.

Seven

Five Men

Death of an Estate Agent

Camps had a small part to play in a small minor tragedy at Cumberland Mansions, an old-fashioned, roomy, red-brick block of flats which fronts George Street, Seymour Place, Brown Street and Nutford Place in what was St Marylebone before it was swept into the City of Westminster. It is a stone's throw from Marble Arch and across the street is the block of flats, slightly grander, in which the former Prince of Wales (later King Edward VIII) met and was entertained by Mrs Simpson. Cato Street, where the early nineteenth century conspirators met to plot an assassination, is not far away. For a respectable building, Cumberland Mansions has had a number of associations with murder and other tragedies. Until thirty years ago it was owned by Sir Edward White, a former chairman of the London County Council, whose wife was senselessly and brutally murdered by Henry Jacoby, an eighteen-year-old pantry boy who was hanged for the crime.

There was a murder in a basement flat on the night of Christmas Day, 1948, the victim being a fifty-year-old, well-liked music hall lightning cartoonist, Harry Saul Michaelson, who was beaten to death with a metal chair as he lay asleep in bed. Harry Lewis, the young thug who did it, was hanged for the crime and Camps performed the post mortem in prison. More recently, a most respected Church of England clergyman missed death by a hair's breadth in another flat when a revolver went off accidentally and a bullet hit him near the groin on a visit to an elderly parishioner.

The tragedy of John D'Agincourt, the assumed name of John Lacaze, who died in a maisonette which forms part of Cumberland Mansions, was that when he was down on his luck he could not face reality. I was a neighbour of D'Agincourt in Cumberland Mansions

171

and knew him well. A shortish, baldish man with the etiolated face of a well-to-do Frenchman, which he was, he was a man of many ideas but did not have the capacity to carry them out. He was also a playboy and numbered among his friends many of the fast-spending socialites who formed the postwar café society in London and Paris.

D'Agincourt had a good war record and had served with the merchant navy in the dangerous waters of the Atlantic and the Far East. Twice his ships had been torpedoed, and each time he was rescued with only the clothes he was wearing. To the rich, good-looking widow whom he met on leave, he was a handsome and romantic figure and they were married before the end of the war.

The reality for John D'Agincourt came when the war ended and, aged forty-six, without a job, training or money, he faced the problem of making a living ashore.

His wife provided the cash for him to buy his way into a small firm of estate agents not far away. He acquired an old but well-kept Bentley and set about expanding the business. There were plenty of clients at that time but the trouble was that there was a chronic shortage of houses and flats to sell. He dabbled in property development both here and in France. I met him in Paris and he told me that he was on the verge of a really big deal, but he left me to pay for the drinks we had had.

But the big deal did not work out. His wife had put up the sum of £33,000 and because of his lack of business experience it had somehow melted away. But worse, a small part of the deficit, amounting to between £2,000 and £3,000, consisted of deposits he had accepted in the ordinary course of business on new houses, some of which had not been built. Arguably, there was a case of fraud to answer, said the police.

The stress of business difficulties and D'Agincourt's wandering eye had by this time caused his marriage to break up, and after the divorce he moved into a bedsitter. When he had no money to pay for that, he saw nothing strange about approaching his ex-wife for help. She refused to throw good money after bad but allowed him back in the flat. The couple remained on friendly terms and whenever he made a few pounds he would treat her to drinks in the local public houses.

In spite of all his troubles, to which he saw no possible solution, he gave all the help he could to bankruptcy officials sorting out his affairs. He continued to dress immaculately, and was full of wry fun. But he was putting on a front, although few of his friends realized it. A summons had been served on him to attend St Marylebone Police Court, fraud being alleged. One evening he rang me and said some newspapers had wind of his troubles and wanted an interview. I advised him to refuse. Next morning, as I left Cumberland Mansions for an early morning stroll, the porter greeted me in an hysterical manner. 'Mr D'Agincourt, sir,' he said. 'Well?' 'He's dead, sir. Died this morning. The doctor has been to see him and they've just taken him away to the mortuary.'

I soon learned what had happened. On the morning he was due to appear at court, the unhappy man had met his wife in the passage at six o'clock, kissed her on the cheek, and returned to his room. Soon afterwards, the maid took him morning tea and could not rouse him. She shouted for her mistress, who telephoned frantically to a mutual doctor friend, a noted T.B. specialist who lived nearby, but there was nothing he could do.

The police at once informed the coroner, Sir Bentley Purchase, who as a boy had also lived in Cumberland Mansions, and with Camps he drove to the maisonette. Later that day, Camps' post mortem showed that D'Agincourt had died from a massive overdose of the sleeping drug nembutal. It seemed to be a clear case of suicide, since there was evidence that D'Agincourt had said that he expected to be sent to prison on a technicality and that he would never face it.

But one fact puzzled Camps. He drew the coroner's attention to peculiar puncture marks on the dead man's left arm, which he said had been caused by a hypodermic syringe. There was no syringe in the flat but during their search for it detectives found two books which threw some light on the affair. One was called *The Miracle of the Human Body* and the other was a detective story in which a character had committed suicide by injecting air into a vein by means of a syringe. Camps said that D'Agincourt might have believed this possible but it was a medical fallacy.

Camps and Purchase puzzled over the missing syringe for some time but came to the conclusion that when D'Agincourt had met his wife that morning, he had just thrown the syringe down the lavatory. I discussed the case several times with Sir Bentley and he always said mysteriously, but without being specific, that there were some 'funny' characters involved. He opened the inquest on 26 September 1958, when Camps was present, and continued it on 7 and 14 October, before deciding formally that John D'Agincourt had killed himself.

A Young Man's Death

It is not uncommon for young provincial girls to find themselves in trouble when they go to London to seek the gay life but young men on the whole seem to manage things rather better. One who did not and who died a terrible death was Fred Hardisty, the twenty-year-old son of a Blackpool coal merchant, who was in London at the beginning of August 1950 practically by accident.

Hardisty was a gifted young man with everything to live for. He had enjoyed his National Service and had made great use of the facilities for sport provided by the army; he was good at rugby, cricket and hockey.

He intended to make his career as a teacher and before he started work his well-to-do father paid for a three-week holiday in France and Switzerland, so that he could brush up his French and German. If the boat train bringing him back from France had not been late, the young man would not have been in London at all on the night of 9 August. He had intended to catch a late night train to Blackpool, but when he realized that he had missed his connection at Euston he decided to see a little of London night life before taking a cheap room for the night in the vicinity of the station.

Chance led him to a continental type of café at the Piccadilly end of Soho, and chance again to a table occupied by a swarthy, well-built man about thirty-five. With his recent experience of life in foreign countries, Hardisty had no qualms about talking to the man, whose free-and-easy manner with the waiters and some of the customers showed that he was a 'regular'. He was, he said, a Greek head-waiter at a Soho club. 'Socrates Petrides,' he introduced himself. To explain why he was there, he said he had just finished for

174

the night and was having a last drink before going home. The young man was soon telling his sad tale, and asking advice about a bed for the night. 'Don't worry, you have fallen on your feet, as we say. I am a bachelor with a flat at 57 Gray's Inn Road which is not very far from here. You must come and stay the night with me.' Anyone a little older and more sophisticated than the young man from Blackpool would have been very wary of such an invitation and would have spotted that the smiling, well-mannered Greek was a homosexual on the look-out for any young man who might come his way.

Petrides suggested a meal before they went to his flat and soon after midnight they took a taxi to Gray's Inn Road. It was Hardisty's last ride. Little less than an hour later, the tenants of the ground floor flat were awakened by shouts and the noise of breaking glass and furniture in the flat above. Hardisty and Petrides were fighting fiercely and must have been fairly evenly matched until the Greek seized a short sword, which was one of three hanging on the wall as ornaments, and began to use it.

Police were too late to save Hardisty, and when Camps arrived at the house with Dr David Matthews, a well-known police surgeon, and a number of detectives, Hardisty was dead in an armchair. The room looked as if a tornado had hit it. Camps found that the sword had been thrust into Hardisty's heart with maniacal force and deduced that he had tottered about the room for a minute, dying and oozing blood as he went.

Petrides told the police that he and Hardisty had drunk some brandy and that the young man had then gone berserk with the sword. It seemed a possible explanation if the young man was not used to taking much drink. But it was noticed that Petrides had several bad scratches on his face and body as if his attacker had been putting up a desperate fight for life and honour. Besides, it was Hardisty who had the sword wound. The police preferred not to believe Petrides, and at the Old Bailey on 26 October he was found guilty of manslaughter and sentenced to five years' imprisonment. It was thought by those concerned with the case that this was a fairly lenient punishment.

The Case of the Frizzled Corpse

Camps' early work in reconstructing apparently unrecognizable bodies was seen at its best in a mysterious case in which a corpse had been frizzled in a London fire in April 1956. The fire blazed in a house in Hampstead Road, in which Colonel Alan Dower, M.P., had lived until it was destroyed by bombing on 10 May 1941. Since then it had been made safe by St Pancras Council, which had requisitioned it, but it was derelict, and vagrants, army deserters and drop-outs in general had been able to find corners here and there at night where they could doss without much police interference.

It was a big house, and a policeman patrolling at 5.45 a.m. noticed smoke coming from the third floor window. As he telephoned for the fire brigade, he made a note of the time. It was a tricky operation to run the hoses up to the third floor but the firemen did so, managed to confine the fire to one room, and soon put it out. The firemen saw at once that the fire had been started and fed by oil and paraffin from drums stored in the room – no one was able to say how the drums came to be in a derelict house – but the policemen who arrived to inspect the damage were not immediately concerned about how the fire had started but about what had been burned.

Among the debris, they found the frizzled corpse of a man. By a fluke, which often happens in fires involving death, the frizzling had left part of the body untouched. In this case, it had stopped short of the feet. It had raged with great intensity around the rest of the body but the feet had been scarcely touched. The dead man had been wearing two pairs of socks and when the coroner was told in addition that the only money found on him was one penny and a farthing, he exclaimed: 'A tramp.'

But, tramp or no tramp, Camps performed the post mortem with his customary thoroughness. He established that the fire had not been started to burn the dead body because the man, about five feet eight inches tall, was alive when the fire started. Death was due to asphyxia. The dead man had no injuries, there was no alcohol in the body and, as Camps proved later, no evidence of poisoning. The pathologist found that the man had a hole in his breast but concluded it was a congenital abnormality and had nothing to do with the man's death.

Camps' detailed reconstruction of the man's physique was so carefully done that the *Police Gazette*, which is circulated to police forces all over the country, was able to publish it as it stood: 'Medium to slight build, high forehead, receding nose, straight possibly aquiline, short upper lip, hair brown slightly tinged with grey, full set of teeth, may have worn spectacles, aged 35-45.'

There was a reason why the police went to such lengths to identify a tramp, who had apparently been burned to death accidentally. Bentley Purchase, the coroner, had already made arrangements to hold an inquest on the frizzled corpse when his officer received a telephone call from Tottenham Court Road Police Station to say that a letter-card had just been received relating to the fire. It apparently came from the victim and read: 'You will be mystified by an accident occurring in the Hampstead Road area which you may suspect to be murder, but it is simply siucide. I am sorry for the damage or trouble I have caused. Fortunately I have no relatives in the South of England to fret.'

It passed through the coroner's mind, as he read the letter, that the inference might be that the dead man had relatives in parts of Britain other than the south of England, and also that suicide by fire must be an exquisitely painful way of ending life; but he let it pass. Chief-Inspector Evan Davies, who brought the letter to Purchase, had obviously something more to tell him.

The letter had not been signed but plainly must have been written before the dead man set fire to himself. The sequence of events, the police thought, might have been that the man had decided to end his life, had written his last letter, possibly at a post office where he would find pen and ink, walked about with it in his pocket for some time, and finally, making the irrevocable decision, had posted it. He had already selected the derelict house as the site of his suicide and eventually set himself on fire. The constable on patrol had seen the smoke at 5.45 a.m. – he had carefully checked the time. 'But,' said Chief-Inspector Davies after telling the story to the coroner, 'the pillar box from which this letter came was cleared before 6.30 a.m. and not again until between 6.30 and 9 a.m. So it is obvious that the letter was posted as much as three hours after the man had died.'

The coroner saw the problem at once. 'The dead man may have

no relatives to fret but others of us are in a rather fretful condition, wondering what happened,' he said.

The letter, ostensibly written by the tramp, was, as the coroner said, 'well cast and grammatical', and the writing fitted neatly on to the card. The word 'suicide', it is true, was wrongly spelled, but that might have been because the writer was rather worried at the prospect of what he was going to do.

At the request of the police, the coroner adjourned the inquest four times for more enquiries to be made, but they produced no results. There were no finger-prints on the anonymous card and no one came forward to identify the handwriting. If it had not been for the card, the coroner would have returned a verdict of accidental death because the police, who had visited the house more than once, had found tramps smoking indoors and even lighting small fires to keep themselves warm. So the coroner's problem, given the indisputable facts provided by Camps was: Accident or suicide? There was a possibility that when the post-box was cleared before 6.30 a.m. the letter-card had been overlooked, but the evidence that that had happened was non-existent. The coroner returned an open verdict. 'I don't like open verdicts,' he said, 'but I am certainly not going to invent any evidence.'

A Policeman is Stabbed

It is generally accepted by people with their fingers on the public pulse that the majority of ordinary British citizens support capital punishment. It is also accepted that those against it are a vociferous and not particularly influential minority, who are expert at manipulating public opinion. When they go into action, they sometimes move mountains.

One of the best examples of the way in which public opinion can be roused and public emotions played upon occurred in 1959 when a young scaffolder, Ronald Henry Marwood, was charged with the murder of an unfledged policeman named Raymond Henry Summers. He was stabbed in the back by Marwood as he tried to stop a gang fight outside Gray's Dance Academy in the rough Seven Sisters Road at Holloway.

Gang fights during the late fifties had become an unpleasant feature of North London night life, but they were usually fights with fists or sticks. Small and silly incidents would be blown up and the flicking of a spill of paper by one gang leader at another in Barry's Dance Hall, Highbury Corner, was enough to arouse bitter feelings of hostility. Such was the childish behaviour of the young North London adults concerned that it was decided to seek immediate revenge.

The fourteenth of December, a Sunday, was the date set for the clash, and this time the gangs armed themselves with razor-edged choppers bought for 2s. 6d. a time, knives, coshes and knuckle-dusters. The gangs lined up on opposite sides of the pavement and were soon locked in bloody battle.

It is not quite clear exactly what part Marwood played in the main struggle. But when the police arrived to break up the screaming mob and Marwood saw Mike Bloom, his friend and best man at his wedding, being led away by a policeman, he went into action. Marwood had armed himself with a ten-inch-long underwater swimmer's knife, 'a murderous weapon', said Mr Christmas Humphreys, who prosecuted. The six feet four inches tall, fair-haired policeman told Marwood to 'clear off' as he approached him threateningly. 'I must have had my hand on the knife which was in my right-hand overcoat pocket,' Marwood was to say. 'I struck out with the intention of pushing him away. The policeman fell down. I stood there for a few seconds. I felt dizzy. My head was spinning. There was no intention to use the knife.'

Intention or not, the knife had been used with tremendous effect. Camps' post mortem showed that it had struck deep and hard. It had penetrated four or five inches into the policeman's body. Such a wound needed a real blow, Camps said. Marwood disappeared and Camps and Sir Bentley Purchase, the coroner in whose area the murder had occurred, followed with interest the ensuing hunt for him. There had been a loud cry of 'He's hit him' and even the yobs fighting the battle were aghast when they saw the young policeman staggering about on his own in the circle they made to watch him. When he fell, they made a mad rush to get away from the scene.

The encounter between Marwood and the policeman had been brief. As P.C. Summers told Marwood to clear off, he swung round with his left arm and caught Marwood with the back of his fist near the top of his left shoulder. Marwood lost his temper and punched back. He then ran down the street, which was a cul de sac, climbed over a garden wall with Bloom and bandaged his hand, which had been cut during the stabbing, while he waited for the noise to die down. He and Bloom concocted a story to tell in case they were stopped by the police, and when this happened they said they had been to the nearby suburb of Manor House. Policemen took them to the police station but they were soon released.

Marwood immediately went on the run, staying most of the time with friends at Chalk Farm, afraid to go out even at night, and reading the stories of the hunt for him in the newspapers. Forty-three days after the stabbing, when Marwood gave himself up, the story was cold and had almost disappeared from the newspapers. The three friends who had been sheltering him had been arrested and, driven from his hiding place, Marwood decided to face up to facts and surrender. The murder weapon had been found near where the stabbing took place and at his Old Bailey trial Marwood's guilt was never in doubt. He had made a statement when he gave himself up which was very nearly a confession of murder: at the very least, it was a confession that his hand had held the knife that killed the police officer. He made a half-hearted attempt to say that he had not used the knife, but Mr Humphreys, in opening the case against him, said the murder was committed 'by one man – Marwood'.

Marwood gave evidence for two and a half hours at his trial. 'Had you anything in your right hand when you hit the policeman?' asked Mr Neil Lawson, who defended Marwood. 'No,' was the answer. 'What happened to the policeman?' Marwood said: 'I noticed he went back a bit and staggered a bit. I took it that it was the force of my punch. I turned and ran away. I realized I had done wrong in hitting a policeman and I imagined that he would be after me.'

Marwood said that when he gave himself up at Caledonian Road Police Station in North London, he made a statement to Superintendent Fenwick, but he did not say in the statement that he had stabbed a policeman. 'I kept on insisting that I never had a knife,' said Marwood, 'but they kept on putting things down.'

'You say you never knew you had a knife in your right-hand pocket and pulled it out when you struck the officer? You did not realize that you had a knife in your hand?' asked Mr Humphreys. When Marwood did not reply, he said: 'I am suggesting this is nonsense. Would you like to put your overcoat on and try?' Marwood insisted that he had not had a knife in his overcoat pocket.

Mr Humphreys again asked Marwood whether he understood the challenge he was putting to him. 'I am going to say it is impossible and you might like the opportunity to put on the overcoat and have a knife like this other weapon to see if it is possible to have that knife in your pocket and not know it.' Marwood declined the challenge. 'I am not concerned whether it is possible or not because I never had a knife.' Marwood also declined to say where he had been staying while on the run.

There is no doubt that the statement Marwood made when he surrendered to the police told heavily against him at his trial. 'I did stab the copper that night,' he had said in the statement, 'I will never know why I did it.'

Was Marwood a victim of circumstances? He was in the sense that if his wife Rosalie had been well they would have celebrated their first wedding anniversary away from North London gangland. Marwood was an ordinary London young man and not a criminal in the accepted sense of the word. He was bright enough to win a scholarship to a grammar school. The only son of an Islington fruit salesman, he had done his National Service in the R.A.S.C. and later became a foreman scaffolder, earning up to £20 a week. There was one small blemish on his character in a conviction for shop-breaking for which he was put on probation; but in the area in which he lived that did not matter overmuch. He was generally regarded as a quiet and well-behaved young man.

The jury, which included two women and a grey-haired man, took two and three-quarter hours to find Marwood guilty of murder, and he became the first man to be sentenced to death under the Homicide Act of 1957 for the murder of a police officer. He was lodged in Pentonville four hundred yards from where he had a room, and the cat-calling and banging of other prisoners at the prison the night before his execution was so disturbing that he asked a warder to go round the cells and tell the prisoners to stop it because he wanted some peace and quiet on the last night of his life. Camps performed the post mortem and naturally found that death was due to judicial hanging.

An Amorous Pole

Of all the people concerned with the murders by a Pole, Hendryk Niemaszes, of Alice Buxton and Hubert Roderick Twells Buxton at the pretty Kentish village of Aldington, Camps had the most straightforward task. The couple were found murdered on the morning of 12 May 1961 by a milkman. Buxton was in the scullery with a bullet in his head and Mrs Buxton was barefooted in the porch, dressed only in an under-slip and cardigan, with such savage injuries that they must have been inflicted by someone in a mad rage. Camps, summoned by the Kent police, said Buxton had died from shock and haemorrhage following the bullet wound and the woman from a fractured skull, brain damage and fractured ribs. Her injuries were caused by a double-barrelled shot gun which had been broken in the process, part of it having been thrown down by the side of the body. The police at first thought that Mrs Buxton had been sexually assaulted but Camps was able to tell them that this was not so.

The task of unravelling a complicated story fell to two of the country's most experienced detectives. Detective-Chief Superintendent James Jenner, as head of the Kent C.I.D., initially took charge but two days later, his chief constable called in from Scotland Yard a famous detective, 'Johnny' Du Rose, later a detective-assistant commissioner, who was assisted by Detective-Sergeant Roy Habershon, later himself to be a detective-chief superintendent.

The community at Aldington was small and it did not take the detectives long to pick up a trail. Two families were involved and both had had tragic experiences during the war. Mrs Buxton, they discovered, was not Mrs Buxton at all. She was really Mrs Bateman, a young Belgian woman who had married Richard Bateman soon after he was demobilized from the army. Bateman fancied an open air life and started a market garden in the fruit-growing district of Evesham. There he met Buxton working as a farm labourer. The men became friends and went into the business together as market gardeners. The Batemans had a house which was bigger than they needed and it seemed more economical for Buxton to lodge with them. It was soon obvious to Buxton that the Bateman marriage was not very happy, and when Alice and Buxton eloped it was practically with Bateman's blessing.

Here Bateman disappears from the story, but there was no fairy-tale ending for Alice. The couple were apparently not sexually compatible and the marriage was falling to pieces when Hendryk Niemaszes appeared on the scene. Niemaszes was the husband of Grypa, a Ukrainian and mother of three children, whom Alice had met on a bus while going to work. The families became friendly and Niemaszes and Alice fell in love.

Once detectives had discovered this, after Alice and Buxton were murdered, it was a short step to the investigation of Niemaszes. Detectives found that Alice and Niemaszes had been meeting clandestinely, but not as secretly as they thought. Later, it was also found that Niemaszes had written letters to Alice in affectionate terms. It was a foregone conclusion that Niemaszes would be found guilty of the double murder when, in addition to bloodstains on his clothes and cycle, the police discovered, under a pile of hay at his house, the gun which was the murder weapon. Niemaszes told a cock-and-bull story of how he had paid a man named George £60 to murder Alice because he was angry with her but the jury, after a trial which lasted four days, took only a little over an hour to find him guilty. He was hanged at Wandsworth on 8 September 1961.

Eight

A Doctor is Acquitted

Towards the end of July 1956, news reached the press room at Scotland Yard that something sensational was afoot at the Sussex seaside town of Eastbourne. The rich widow of a Lloyd's under-writer, Mrs Gertrude Joyce Hullett, had died in her mansion at the top of Beachy Head. The celebrated but enigmatic Professor Francis Camps had been seen carrying a bag containing the tools of his trade. He was said to have conducted a post mortem which had lasted 'several hours', though Camps had never been known to spend that length of time on a single post mortem. It was also said that he had given evidence at an inquest but no one could be sure because, mysteriously, the inquest had been held at the police station and not at the town hall where inquests were normally held. The rumours died down but they were revived again in December when it became known that a well-known, popular Irish doctor of the town, John Bodkin Adams, had been arrested, not for the murder of Mrs Hullett but for that of eighty-one-year-old Edith Alice Morrell, also a rich widow.

In March the following year Dr Adams was tried, more than six years after Mrs Morrell had died, and the trial was reported all over the world. To prosecute him at the Old Bailey, the Crown assembled a strong team. The Attorney-General was later to become Lord Chancellor Dilhorne and his assistant, Melford Stevenson, a High Court judge. A few years later, Mr Geoffrey Lawrence, Q.C., who was instructed by the Medical Defence Union for Dr Adams, was also to be made a judge.

The case produced a most curious situation, said Mr Justice Devlin, the trial judge, because the act of murder had to be proved by expert evidence – medical evidence which was an essential part of the case and 'perhaps the crucial part'.

The case lasted seventeen days and became the longest murder trial recorded in the history of Britain. The legal advisers for the defence decided not to call Dr Adams himself and the jury must have thought the case against him was so thin that it took only forty-five minutes to find him not guilty of murder.

Camps was called to give evidence as an expert but his testimony was not the normal sort of evidence he gave. He had not performed the post mortem on Mrs Morrell because there was no body. It had been cremated at Downs Crematorium, Brighton, shortly after death.

The prosecution's case depended largely on the evidence of the Crown's specialist medical witness, Dr Arthur Henry Douthwaite, and of the nurses who had attended Mrs Morrell during her last illness. Since the nurses spoke of events that had happened more than six years before, there was, understandably, some conflict between what they had written in their reports at the time and their recollections at the trial.

The Attorney-General opened strongly at the Old Bailey, saying that Dr Adams, who was then fifty-eight, had killed Mrs Morrell by the administration of drugs to her and that the drugs were given with the intention of killing. Dr Adams had been Mrs Morrell's doctor from 1949. Two years earlier Mrs Morrell, an habitual will maker, then paralysed as a result of a stroke and very frail, had made a will. Six months later she made another, which was to be followed by another, plus a codicil. In none of the wills was there any bequest to Dr Adams. Mrs Morrell had been in a nursing home in April 1949 but when she was back in her own home, being nursed and treated with morphine and heroin, Dr Adams telephoned Mr Sogno, her solicitor, to say that Mrs Morrell was extremely anxious about the contents of her latest will and wanted to see him that day. Mr Sogno went to see her and as a result she made yet another will in which she bequeathed Dr Adams an oak chest containing silver.

Mrs Morrell was a wealthy woman, worth at least £150,000, and the bequest could hardly be described as munificent. As Mr Lawrence was to say later, it was ludicrous to suggest that Dr Adams should have anticipated Mrs Morrell's death by a few days or weeks for a chest of silver valued at £270.

Early in 1950 there were further negotiations between Mrs Morrell's solicitor and her doctor, and the Attorney-General described how Dr Adams had called on Mr Sogno and told him Mrs Morrell had promised to give him a Rolls Royce in her will. She now remembered that she had forgotten it. 'He said she desired to give him, not only the Rolls Royce, but the contents of a case of jewellery in the bank,' said Sir Reginald. Dr Adams suggested that Mr Sogno should prepare a codicil which should be executed and later destroyed if it did not meet with Mrs Morrell's son's approval. Other wills or codicils left Dr Adams her house, personal chattels, the Rolls Royce and an Elizabethan cupboard, all with the proviso that her son must have predeceased her.

The drugs, morphine and heroin, prescribed in the period 7-10 November and again between 10 and 12 November, given by the nurses and by Dr Adams himself, on his own prescriptions, were detailed by Attorney-General Sir Reginald Manningham-Buller.

'Mrs Morrell died in the early hours of 13 November. The amount of morphine given during 7-10 November was nearly double the previous prescription of morphine. The heroin prescribed in that period was the largest prescription up to that date. What had happened to Mrs Morrell necessitating this tremendous increase in a prescription of these dangerous drugs?' asked the Attorney-General. 'She was not in acute pain. The Crown submits that Dr Adams prescribed these quantities because he had decided that the time had come for Mrs Morrell to die.'

The Crown obviously thought it sinister that on 13 November Dr Adams had filled in a form to secure Mrs Morrell's cremation. One of the questions on the form for the certifying doctor to answer was: 'Have you, as far as you are aware, any pecuniary interest in the death of the deceased?' Dr Adams had replied to the question: 'Not as far as I am aware.' When later, in the course of Scotland Yard enquiries, Detective-Superintendent Herbert Hannam drew Dr Adams' attention to the answer, his reply was, 'Oh, that was not done wickedly. God knows it was not. We always want cremations to go off smoothly for the sake of relatives.'

Dr Adams had also told Mr Hannam that the 'poor soul' had been in terrible agony. Yet, the Attorney-General said, the nurses would tell the court that before her death Mrs Morrell had been comatose for days and had not been suffering pain.

Sir Reginald listed four facts which he said would be conclusively established. The first was that Mrs Morrell died after two large injections of drugs had been given on Dr Adams' instructions. The second was that, then in a coma, she was suffering from spasms and that this was an indication of a heavy dosage of heroin or morphine or both. The third was that Dr Adams had told Detective-Superintendent Hannam that there were no drugs left over when she died and that Mrs Morrell had had them all because he had given them to her. The fourth fact was that no less than 8 grammes of heroin had been prescribed on 8 November and that the maximum quantity of heroin which should have been prescribed for a period of twenty-four hours was $\frac{1}{4}$ gramme.

Six days before Christmas, 1956, Dr Adams was arrested at his home. When told the charge was murder, he said: 'Murder? Murder? Can you prove it was murder? I don't think you can prove murder. She was dying in any event.'

On the second day of the trial, three pharmaceutical chemists were called to certify formally that Dr Adams had given prescriptions for the drugs Mrs Morrell had taken. Nurses followed them into the witness box to describe the closing days of the old lady's life.

Mrs Morrell was neurotic and weak, said the first nurse, Miss Helen Rose Stronach. The nurse remembered that the doctor had given her injections when he visited her late in the evenings, though she neither saw the injections actually given nor knew what they were.

The first surprising admission Miss Stronach made was when Mr Lawrence cross-examined her on the entries made in her report books. She agreed the entries showed that Mrs Morrell was having brandy and sedormid and not morphine or any other injection from the doctor. Nor had she ever recorded Dr Adams' evening visits to Mrs Morrell when she was on duty, although she had said her reports contained a record of every injection given and everything of significance in the patient's illness, injection medicine and the doctor's visits.

Mr Lawrence suggested that Nurse Stronach's memory had

187

played her a trick when she said she had never injected anything. 'Yes, it is a long time ago to remember these things,' she said.

'Let us face this,' said Mr Lawrence, 'it is another complete trick of your memory to say that on the last day you left, Mrs Morrell was either semi-conscious and rambling, now you see what you wrote down at the time, isn't it?'

'I have nothing to say,' said the nurse, and repeated her answer when pressed by Mr Lawrence.

Mr Lawrence again refreshed the nurse's memory from the medical records she and her colleagues made at the time and said it was obviously quite inaccurate to say Mrs Morrell was unconscious and rambling on the day she left. 'Well, I have always believed she was, as far as my memory was concerned,' she said.

'Maybe,' rejoined Mr Lawrence. 'But having looked at these notes written down six years ago, with no memory at all, it is quite clear it is wrong to say that she was semi-conscious and rambling. Or was it not?'

'Apparently so,' admitted the nurse.

The second nurse, Sister Annie Helen Mason-Ellis, said she could not remember whether, when she first went to Mrs Morrell's, the patient was having injections of any kind. Sir Reginald pointed out that there was an entry in the nurses' book for 27 June 1950 that Mrs Morrell had been given an injection of morphine in the evening on the instructions of Dr Adams. The sister said that when Dr Adams visited Mrs Morrell the nurses were asked to leave the room, and she could not remember ever seeing Dr Adams give an injection to Mrs Morrell. 'It is too long ago,' she said. 'Right from the start in August 1949, Mrs Morrell had been under routine sedation. That was maintained for months and months and months, without alteration.'

Mr Lawrence asked the sister what was the first word she had written in her report for the afternoon of 12 November 1950. 'It was "awake", followed by "but quiet".' Sister Mason-Ellis agreed that the report showed that Mrs Morrell was not in a coma.

There were two nurses with Mrs Morrell when she died and their evidence was in much the same terms. Mrs Caroline Randall said Mrs Morrell was not suffering severe pain but her limbs were stiff because she had been unable to use them for some time. On

188

7 November Mrs Morrell was getting bigger quantities of heroin, morphine and a drug called omnopon. Mrs Randall said her reports for the next few days recorded the increasing administration of drugs. On the night of her death, Mrs Morrell was weak, semi-conscious and shaken by spasms. Dr Adams gave the patient a 5 c.c. injection of paraldehyde. He then re-filled the syringe and said that if Mrs Morrell became restless she should give the injection to her. The injection Dr Adams himself gave kept Mrs Morrell quiet for about an hour and then the spasms became worse. 'I thought it too soon to give the patient another injection,' said Mrs Randall. 'I tried to telephone Dr Adams but he was out. In the end, I gave the patient the other injection.'

Nurse Randall said both Dr Adams and his partner, Dr R. V. Harris, had been treating Mrs Morrell, and when Dr Adams was away Dr Harris continued the treatment he had been giving. Confronted with a spell of restlessness at night, Dr Harris increased the drugs and introduced omnopon. Later, Dr Harris agreed that this had been so. He did it because Mrs Morrell was in an extremely irritable state over Dr Adams being away.

The other nurse, Mrs Bartlett, said she did not observe severe pain in the patient but she remembered that on the last night of Mrs Morrell's life Dr Adams had given her an injection, though she could not remember what it was. The nurse's report for 9 October was produced by Mr Lawrence, who drew attention to the entry 'Query – Stroke?' The nurse agreed that from that time onward Mrs Morrell was going downhill.

The judge intervened during Mrs Randall's evidence to ask if Mrs Morrell had been in a coma during the last three or four nights. 'Not a coma,' said the nurse, 'but a sleep like a coma.'

Mr Lawrence's further cross-examination was directed to the injections Mrs Morrell had had before she died. Answering his questions, Mrs Randall said that at 10.30 p.m. she had recorded an injection of 5 c.c. of paraldehyde by Dr Adams but there was no record of any subsequent injection. 'It is just not conceivable, is it, that you have left out of the record an injection if, in fact, it was ever given?' he asked. 'I did give it,' was the nurse's reply.

'You cannot have it both ways,' said Mr Lawrence. 'If it is a matter of any importance, it would have gone into the book?'

The answer was 'Yes'. After further questions, Mr Lawrence remarked: 'Your memory is not trustworthy, is it?' 'It appears not to be,' agreed Mrs Randall.

At this stage of the trial – the fifth day – it was apparent that the judge was having doubts about the strength of the case against Dr Adams. He asked the Attorney-General: 'Are you going to invite the jury to say that the last two or one – whichever it was – injections of 5 c.c. paraldehyde were given or caused to be given by Dr Adams with the intention of causing the death of Mrs Morrell?'

'I submit that they were given deliberately by Dr Adams,' said Sir Reginald, 'and that they accelerated the death of the patient. But I won't elaborate, my lord. I adhere to that and my medical evidence will indicate why.'

The prosecution's main case took nearly seven days to present, but a little tidying-up remained. Mrs Morrell's chauffeur for three years testified that he had received £1,000 under her will, and Mr Hubert Sogno, her solicitor, said that when Mrs Morrell died Dr Adams was not a beneficiary in the final will. He had been given the Elizabethan chest and Rolls Royce by favour of Mrs Morrell's son because it was his mother's last wish. Her will also stipulated that she should be cremated.

The evidence of the Crown's medical expert, Harley Street specialist Dr A. H. Douthwaite, senior physician at Guy's Hospital, occupied several days, and in the closing stages he summarized it briefly. He was asked by Mr Lawrence: 'As a doctor and specialist yourself, you are saying that he [Adams] formed the intention to terminate her life on 8 November and carried that intention into effect over the next five days?' Dr Douthwaite answered 'Yes.'

'A specialist's profession is a responsible one, no doubt, but I hardly suppose you have often expressed a graver or more fateful opinion on a matter of medicine than that, have you?' The answer was 'No'.

Mrs Morrell had had a stroke and Dr Douthwaite began his evidence by describing three common causes of strokes. They were haemorrhage of the brain, cerebral thrombosis and cerebral embolism. He said severe haemorrhage almost always resulted in death in three or four days. Victims of cerebral thrombosis and embolism usually survived and their condition would improve spontaneously over several months. A patient could survive for many years after such complaints.

Dr Douthwaite said he had seen the reports of Mrs Morrell's nurses. 'What is your opinion as to the cause of the stroke from which Mrs Morrell suffered in 1948?' asked the Attorney-General. 'In all probability, a cerebral thrombosis.'

'I want you to indicate quite briefly what is the proper course of treatment for a patient who has suffered a stroke as a result of coronary thrombosis?' The answer was: 'Within a few days, as soon as one is able to, in co-operation with the patient, or when the mind is clear as it may well be within a few days, one should do one's best to mobilize the patient, encourage movement of the body and indeed encourage her to try to move the paralysed part, with massage and so forth.'

The prescription list for 21 July, 1948 was examined and it contained heroin and morphine sulphate. 'Is there, in your opinion any justification for injecting morphine and heroin immediately after a stroke for cerebral haemorrhage?' 'There is no justification.'

'Is it right or wrong to do so?' asked the Attorney-General. 'It is wrong. In all circumstances it would be wrong to inject heroin and morphine.'

'What about morphine alone?' 'Morphine alone should not be given to someone who has had a stroke, unless there was an episode of acute mania. Then it would be justified as a single injection.'

Asked to describe the effect of morphine and heroin on Mrs Morrell's rehabilitation, Dr Douthwaite said it would greatly interfere with any progress.

He gave the jury a short description of the uses, values and disadvantages of the two drugs and said they would result in chest complications. Morphine was also powerfully constipating. Irritability would soon pass off but he would expect, in a patient of eighty-one, some degree of cerebral arterio-sclerosis. It would be quite wrong in that case to administer morphine because addiction would be rapidly caused and because there were many other safer drugs which were more effective. Since 1950 bromides, barbitones and many barbiturates had been available. The administration of morphine and heroin together, regularly, over a short period of time, would probably produce drowsiness and sleep to start with.

But, on recovery from that, the patient, on wakening, would feel ill, irritable, and possibly sick and might vomit. 'The patient's reaction to the feeling of pleasure was one of dependence on the doctor who naturally obtains complete ascendancy over the patient, once addiction has occurred.'

Dr Douthwaite said morphine and heroin were dangerous drugs, both in the legal and medical senses. Asked to compare the two, he said heroin was a stronger drug, though morphine was more dangerous. Heroin's action in many respects was similar to that of morphine, but it differed in important respects. The effect of heroin on respiration was that it was a powerful depressant on what doctors called the respiratory centre of the brain. Heroin was three or four times more powerful as a depressant. It would facilitate sleep by removing pain but twitching of the limbs could be induced by it. Barbiturates would tend to depress or prevent that, if adequately applied. Heroin stimulated the spinal cord much more constantly and violently than morphine, the visible effect being twitching or convulsions.

'The natural tolerance of human beings to heroin and morphine varies but would develop very quickly within a fortnight or three weeks of routine administration,' said Dr Douthwaite.

He said that if the administration to an addicted patient were stopped, the patient became ill and wildly excited, getting pain in the limbs, sweating, sneezing and possible collapse – a whole host of what were known as withdrawal symptoms. These became maximal if morphine and heroin were withheld for about two days.

Dr Douthwaite said that curing an addiction was a very unpleasant process for the patient. Maintaining routine injections of morphine and heroin at the same level for a long period would produce suffering. 'It would keep the patient in almost constant craving for more drugs and thus ensure that she would be excitable, bad-tempered and impossible to live with,' he said.

Omnopon, said the witness, contained fifty per cent of morphine and had a similar effect to morphine. Paraldehyde was a sedative and its distinguishing feature was a revolting smell and taste. It also acted as a depressant on the respiratory system and the whole of the central nervous system.

The Attorney-General asked: 'What would be the effect if it

was used to stop twitching, if it was superimposed on heavy administration of heroin alone or heroin and morphine?' The doctor's sombre reply was that it would be likely to produce death. 'It is not in itself a dangerous drug but it would deepen coma or heavy sleep, if that existed,' he said.

'Is there any justification or legitimate ground for administering morphine and heroin?' asked the Attorney-General. The answer was 'No'.

'What is the object of the administration of heroin?' 'To keep her thoroughly doped or drugged.'

A little later, Dr Douthwaite was asked whether there was anything in the nurses' reports or the evidence he had heard to justify the administration of heroin and morphine on 10, 11 and 12 November. 'There is nothing,' he said.

'Did you find any evidence of her suffering severe pain since her stroke?' asked Sir Reginald. 'No,' said Dr Douthwaite, 'a condition of severe pain following a stroke occurs very rarely and is known as the Thalmic syndrome. There is no indication in the reports of any such complaint.'

The Attorney-General asked: If the prescriptions for November exceeded the amounts shown in the nurses' reports and the difference was, in fact, administered to Mrs Morrell in that period, what effect would that have had on her prospect of life. 'They would have killed her,' was the reply.

Sir Reginald raised the question of the cremation form in which Dr Adams had recorded that the immediate cause of death was coronary thrombosis. 'Are there any signs in the nurses' reports, in your opinion, which would justify that conclusion?' The answer was 'No'.

Even more emphatic was the answer to the question: 'Supposing there had been any signs of cerebral haemorrhage in November, would there have been any justification for administering this dose of heroin?' 'No, certainly not,' said Dr Douthwaite.

'In your opinion, should heroin be administered to old people?' 'No,' said the doctor.

Dr Douthwaite was cross-examined about the possibility of giving safer drugs, such as hyocine, instead of morphine and heroin. He said hyocine was a drug which produced sleep; it tended to soothe rather than excite. 'The injection of hyocine with morphine in this case would have been dangerous?' Mr Lawrence suggested. The answer was 'No'.

In the last stages of cerebral irritation, with a considerable reduction of morphine and heroin, there were several drugs which could be given and were safer, he said. 'I know what your opinion has been over these last days,' said Mr Lawrence, 'but at least it is a possible alternative view on these reports [nursing records] that this general practitioner was following a consistent course with these drugs to produce the result which was his duty to produce? When he found he could not do it on the last day and night, he tried to turn to something else?' 'Yes,' answered Dr Douthwaite.

'Going through the details of these reports, there is no necessity at all to postulate a murderous intent at any time, is there?' Dr Douthwaite answered. 'There is, in my opinion, evidence of intent to terminate life.'

After further questions, Mr Lawrence said: 'If you won't go the whole way with me, at any rate you will go some of the way in agreeing with me with regard to the possible alternative view I have put to you?' Dr Douthwaite's answer was 'yes', but he added that it was a matter of medical opinion.

The judge intervened. 'Here is a man who attempts to kill and it has now gone on for some time and failed,' he said. 'He drops morphia and keeps half a grain of heroin. You are quite satisfied, are you, that the only conclusion you can draw from that is that half a grain of heroin is intended to kill?' 'That is my view,' agreed the doctor.

A little later the judge said: 'You are forced to the conclusion that Dr Adams gave paraldehyde because he was tired of waiting for heroin and morphine to act and bring quick results?' 'Yes,' was the answer.

'Your view is really this: that the first time the design of murder emerges from the medical pattern is when he drops morphine and concentrates on heroin?' 'Yes.'

'The only possible medical explanation for that being that he intends to re-introduce morphine with lethal effects?'

The answer again was 'yes' and Dr Douthwaite said that if a post mortem had been held the morphine and heroin would have been found in her body.

A consultant neurologist at six London hospitals, Dr M. G. C. Ashby, agreed that the possibility of Mrs Morrell's death being due to natural causes could not be ruled out and another doctor, John B. Harman of Harley Street, for the defence, said that the drug doses given to Mrs Morrell were not freak doses.

'Dr Adams had not turned to hyocine as an alternative but to paraldehyde,' said Mr Lawrence. 'Can you think of anything better or safer that he could have turned to?' The answer was: 'That is what I would have done if I had to turn to something.'

Camps' evidence was given on the thirteenth day of the trial and he was called by the Attorney-General to deal with a number of points raised by the judge.

Camps said the signatures of two doctors are required on a cremation form and that if a medical referee (i.e. a second doctor) refused to sign a cremation certificate, having had the necessary forms completed by one doctor, the referee could order a post mortem himself or, more commonly, notify the coroner who could order a post mortem to be carried out under his own auspices. In either event, as a result of that post mortem, the certificate 'F', which would be signed by the pathologist or doctor carrying out the post mortem, would supersede the 'B' and 'C' certificates, or, in the absence of the coroner, the post mortem certificate would cancel out the other two and his certificate would then be accepted by the referee. If a person definitely expressed a desire to be cremated, he thought it obligatory for that to be done.

Camps explained, when he was cross-examined, that the medical referee, when he had examined the forms submitted to him, could order a post mortem at his discretion, but this was usually done only in the case of technical difficulties; for example, if a person had not been seen by a doctor in the prescribed time before death. If the doctor communicated with the coroner, the coroner would undertake an investigation, with statements being taken from the various people concerned, and he might then order a post mortem. 'In the case of a cremation,' said Camps, 'it is now always the practice to order a post mortem because cremation is the final act. Having assessed the evidence, the coroner then holds an inquest if he thinks fit and he is entitled to sign a cremation certificate after due enquiries without an inquest, if he is satisfied there is no suspicion, or that death has not resulted from an accident or anything of that sort.'

The judge questioned Camps about the feelings of relatives regarding post mortems. Camps said a situation could arise, although he had not met it personally, whereby, if a doctor had been left a legacy under a will, the relatives might say, 'We would much rather she was buried and we believe that would be her own wish rather than that a post mortem be carried out.' His own experience, said Camps, had been that in such a case the medical referee automatically notified the coroner.

In his summing up, Mr Justice Devlin said it would be utterly wrong if the jury were to regard Dr Adams' silence, (i.e. he had not gone into the witness box) as contributing in any way towards proof of guilt.

After the jury had found Dr Adams not guilty, the Attorney-General announced that the Crown would not proceed on a further indictment charging Dr Adams with the murder of Mrs Hullett.

Other charges, with which Camps was not concerned, were dealt with separately.

Nine

Camps on Jack the Ripper

The grisly murders committed by the sadistic maniac nicknamed Jack the Ripper in the year 1888 aroused Camps' interest, and held it to the end of his life, for a number of reasons. As a pathologist, he was curious about the nature of the terrible and unusual injuries inflicted on the victims. As a criminologist, he was fascinated by the fact that the murderer could perpetrate certainly five, and possibly many more, messy murders in a crowded though admittedly badly lighted area, and escape. As a lecturer and speaker whose talk was often spiced with references to the case, he was concerned to examine and comment on all the exhibits, especially those in the London Hospital in Whitechapel, East London, where he worked and near which most of the murders were committed in the squalid streets or lodging houses around it.

Many books and articles have been written about the Ripper, but, in view of the perennial interest in the misdeeds of this unidentified man, the known facts, and even some of the speculations, are worth recapitulating.

The murders all took place within a few weeks in the second half of 1888. The murdered women were prostitutes, one as young as twenty-four and the oldest double that age. They were not physically attractive women. Cheap gin had ruined their complexions and bloated their faces. Because the clients were poor, their prices had to be low – they still were in the late thirties: an old crone once accosted me when I was on an assignment in the dock area and offered her services for sixpence. They operated in the alleys that proliferate east of Aldgate pump. Their homes were the smelly dosshouses where beds cost no more than pence. But often the prostitutes were so far below the poverty line that the nightly charge was beyond their means. Mrs Mary Ann 'Polly' Nicholls, one of the victims, being refused admission to a doss-house because she could not pay the full price of a bed, set out to earn the money in the early hours of the morning and was murdered by the Ripper.

The women were well-known to the philosophic street traders and scallywags who hung about the street corners waiting to pick up an honest or dishonest penny. They could even whistle in the dark and joke about the Ripper. 'I'm for Jack tonight,' one was reported to have jested as she set out on her rounds. They answered to picturesque names. One redhead was Carrotty Nell; a woman who habitually smoked a clay pipe was 'Clay Pipe' Alice. The East End of those days was a testing and terrible district to live in. Unnatural death was as commonplace as poverty, vice and premature old age. When I was going through post mortem reports of even a later period, I came across a pathologist's report in which he said that he had examined the body of an 'old man of 33'. But even the easy-going and hardened Cockneys, both men and women, felt chilled with terror when the Ripper started his work.

It is still very difficult to be sure which of the women who were murdered and mutilated in the Ripper's time were really his victims. Murders, especially those of a sexual nature, are known to excite men with abnormal appetites to commit duplicates. We are dealing with events which happened nearly a century ago and, as Daniel Farson, a careful writer who once kept a public house just outside the area where the women were murdered, pointed out in his recent book *Jack the Ripper*, writers on the subject have for years borrowed indiscriminately from each other. 'Facts which aren't so,' to quote Bret Harte, find their way into print, are repeated without verification, and become accepted as true.

Sir Melville Macnaghten, who as head of the Metropolitan CID at the time was in a position to know better than anyone, considered the Ripper murdered five times: once on the last day of August (Mary Ann Nicholls), once on 8 September (Annie Chapman), twice on 30 September (Elizabeth Stride and Catherine Eddowes) and finally on 9 November (Mary Kelly). Colin Wilson, a well-known writer in other fields, who has spent years studying the Ripper murders – according to Camps, Wilson knows more about the subject than anybody – adds a footnote. In his *Encyclo-*

paedia of Murder he says that some writers and criminologists consider the Ripper killed twice more; on 3 April (Emma Elizabeth Smith) and on 7 August (Martha Turner or sometimes Tarbram). Wilson is inclined to doubt it.

A number of criminologists with more imagination than sense have also linked with the Ripper the murder in Whitechapel of a young prostitute, Frances Cole. She had Ripper-type injuries including a cut throat. But her murder occurred on 13 February 1891, more than two years after the Ripper was thought to have claimed his last victim. With his immense medical knowledge to back his opinion, Camps has pointed out that murderers like the Ripper do not 'burn out'; they kill at regular intervals until they die, emigrate or are incarcerated. Two years would be a long time for a murderer like the Ripper to lie low before he started murdering again.

If the Ripper died soon after what Sir Melville considered his last murder on 9 November 1888, another unfortunate woman, Mrs Alice McKenzie, cannot have been his victim, although she had had her throat slit and had other injuries. 'Clay Pipe' Alice was a part-time prostitute. The date of her death was 17 July 1889. The strong possibility is that the two were carbon copy murders, probably committed by a violent seaman named Thomas Sadler. A typical 'drunken sailor' when on leave, the police were aware that he knew the two women but they had not enough evidence to arrest him.

Apart from the actual fact of the murders themselves, what shocked and terrified the public during the Ripper's short reign of terror was the increasing ferocity with which he went about his work.

The body of the first victim was mutilated badly enough. She had been disembowelled and the mortuary attendant almost collapsed when he saw all the injuries. There were four main stab wounds, two at the throat which severed the wind-pipe and two upward thrusts at the abdomen. The attack must have been made so quickly and without warning that Mrs Nicholls had no time to scream.

A more horrible spectacle was to await the finder of the body of Mrs Annie Chapman. Her head had been almost cut off then tied back in place with a cloth. The lower part of her trunk had been ripped open and the intestines draped on her shoulder. The pathologist searched for the womb, bladder and intestines but could not find them. The coroner at the inquest cleared his court to hear the gruesome evidence and agreed with the pathologist that the horrible mutilations were the work of an expert.

The 'simple' throat-cutting of the next victim, Elizabeth Stride, was attributed to the fact that the Ripper was almost caught in the act and had to flee. But less than half an hour later he was at work with his knife on the body of Catherine Eddowes, and dreadful photographs the police took showed the effect to which he had used it. The woman's body had to be stitched up from her cut throat to her stomach and the appalling thrusts had continued around her private parts. Her face had been cut and bruised and as usual the kidneys and other organs were missing. 'She was like a pig ripped open for market,' said the police constable who discovered the body. The unfortunate woman, when the attacker struck, must have thought she was experiencing an attack of *delirium tremens*; until a few minutes before her death, she had been held for her own safety in a police cell in Bishopsgate on a charge of drunkenness.

All the four murders so far had been committed in the open air but the last victim was butchered indoors. She was Mrs Mary Kelly, a one-time failed actress, Irish, feckless, drunken and penniless. She did not deserve her fate, which was worse than that of all the others. When she was found after shouts of 'murder' had been heard earlier from her room, the bloody remains could not be identified as female until her cut-off breasts were spotted on a table. Her head lay beside the body on a dirty pillow. Her face was completely un-recognizable. The entrails appeared to have been wrenched out by hand from the body and flung at the picture rail, from which some still hung. A young detective named Dew, who later in life found the remains of Dr Crippen's wife in a cellar and arrested Crippen and his mistress Ethel Le Neve as they stepped on Canadian soil, went to the scene with his inspector. The sight, he said in his reminis-cences, was the most gruesome memory of his whole career.

If the press reports of the time are to be believed, the state of London can be described truthfully as panic-stricken. There were few serious clues to the murders but on the flimsiest of evidence, or on no evidence but merely hearsay, the excitable East Enders were ready to lynch suspects. Ordinary women kept indoors after dark. A man carrying a black tool-bag was said to have been seen leaving the street where one of the murders had been committed. Word went around Whitechapel quickly and every carrier of a black bag had to run for his life from the mob.

The newspapers thundered for action and Police Commissioner Sir Charles Warren, as bewildered as everybody else, was panicked into taking foolish measures, which included bringing bloodhounds into the area after the murder of Miss Kelly – his last act before re-signing. More sensibly, the Home Secretary offered to grant a free pardon to any accomplice who would give the Ripper away. It must have been addressed to the non-existent because there were no takers.

The hoaxers soon became busy, as they still often do when murders take place, writing misleading letters to the newspapers and the police. But when a small kidney arrived at the home of the Whitechapel Vigilance Committee chairman, with a note pro-claiming it to be from a victim, the police chiefs and the newspapers could not make up their minds whether it was sent by the Ripper, as he signed himself, or by someone with a perverted sense of humour. The pathologist who examined it, however, thought it might have come from the body of Catherine Eddowes. It showed evidence of Bright's disease, which can be caused by heavy gin drinking. Mrs Eddowes was a gin addict and her kidneys were missing.

It is generally understood by all who have studied the Ripper murders that all theories about the identity of Jack are theories and nothing else. Such 'evidence' as supports them would never stand up in a court of law. The varied suspects can be lined up for in-spection: an heir to the throne of England, a doctor or his son, a royal doctor, a former Polish doctor's assistant, a ritual slaughterer, another doctor who was not suspected by the police, and a motley miscellany, including a barrister.

Camps himself did not accept the theory that the killer must necessarily have been a doctor or a man with medical training because of the nature of the injuries inflicted on the dead women. Medical training, he used to say, was not needed to wield the sharp knife used in the killings, and many unqualified people would have the elementary knowledge of anatomy needed to sever internal organs, if they had the nerve to use their knowledge. These operations were crude. 'Any surgeon who operated in this manner would have been struck off the medical register,' Camps has written.

Looking from this distance of time, it is scarcely credible that, on the basis of the garbled gossip of Dr Thomas Stowell, an old seeker after notoriety on a television programme, the theory that the Ripper was the young Duke of Clarence, then heir to the throne, should have been considered for a moment. Yet this happened. Stowell, having set the rumour on its way, then refused publicly to confirm that he actually referred to the duke on television, although privately he repeated the statement to several people interested in the Ripper case.

Shortly, his story was that the duke was heterosexual and contracted syphilis either from a young sailor while on a round-the-world naval cruise with his brother, later George V, or from a white woman in the West Indies, after a party. On his return to England, he took his revenge on the sort of diseased women who had caused his misfortune. Camps, in his analysis of the case, discarded both that theory and the equally improbable gossip that the murderer was Sir William Gull, an eminent royal physician. A well-known writer, Michael Harrison, in his book *Clarence*, goes fully into the allegations against the duke; the flaws apparently are that the dates do not fit in. When the murders took place, the duke seems to have been at either Balmoral or Sandringham.

The story that traduced Gull was based on the information given to Stowell by a spiritualist named Lees, who admitted he had dreamt it! It was a cruel slander. The known fact is that Gull had been completely incapacitated by a stroke in 1887 before the Ripper murders began.

The old and for years popular theory that the murders were committed by a 'Dr Stanley', out of revenge for the infection with syphilis of his son by Mary Kelly, seems to have been believed by an MP named Leonard Matters, but hardly anybody else. Matters told the story of Stanley's death-bed confession in Buenos Aires with melodramatic detail. Stanley was said to have summoned a former favourite student to his room and asked if he had heard of Jack the Ripper. The student nodded. 'Well, I am he,' said Stanley, and died. Nobody who has investigated the facts believes what is generally accepted as a piece of fiction.

The name of the bogus doctor Neil Cream has been associated with the Ripper murders. The evidence against him rests on four words spoken on the gallows but it is bolstered by the fact that Cream also preyed on prostitutes and killed them, although not quickly with the knife but with slow-acting poison.

Cream's criminal career was lengthened and protected because he had a double with whom he was in league. The great advocate Sir Edward Marshall Hall believed he had come across Cream before the Ripper murders, when he defended him at Bow Street on a charge of bigamy. The evidence was waiting in the court-room in the shape of several attractive young women. But the man in the dock asserted that he could not have been guilty because he was in Australia when the offences were supposed to have been committed.

This was before the days of Interpol, and the sceptical Metropolitan Police therefore sent a cable to Australia giving the man's description and asking for verification of his story. The prison governor confirmed that a man of the description given had been in prison in Sydney and the accused was set free.

When Cream was finally brought to trial, Marshall Hall was in court and exclaimed on the similarity between him and the man acquitted of bigamy. He came up with the explanation of the double. Cream was not so lucky at the murder trial. He was sentenced to death. A couple of seconds before the hangman sprang the trap, Cream is supposed to have said 'I am Jack the ...' His neck was broken before he could complete the sentence but, in the opinion of Marshall Hall, it would really have made no difference if he had done so. The Ripper had great prestige among the criminal class and many villains before Cream and after him made similar claims.

'Vanity is an inherent disease in murderers,' said Marshall Hall, who had known plenty in his time. 'If Cream had been allowed to complete his sentence I should personally not have believed him. I should have regarded it as another exhibition of the murderer's vanity.'

George Chapman, another suspect, involved the large alien East End population in the mystery of the Ripper. A man of many names, he began life as Severine Klosoffski in the Warsaw Jewish ghetto. As a *faldscher*, or doctor's assistant, he acquired some knowledge of medicine (and of poisons) and when as a young married man he reached Whitechapel, where the opportunities for a smart Pole were believed to be greater, he set up as a barber in a basement near where Martha Turner was murdered. There he met a man named Pedachenco, whose close friend he became. Suspicion fell on both men, especially when it became known that Chapman was an ex-*faldscher*, who was now doing a little doctoring as well as barbering. But if knifing women was not Chapman's line, it became clear later that he had murderous instincts of a different sort. Allegations that he might be the Ripper faded, but three years after the Ripper murders Chapman, by now a publican, was convicted of the poisoning of several women, the famous Public Prosecutor Sir Archibald Bodkin being so outraged at the murders that he spent thousands of pounds tracing sixty witnesses to secure Chapman's conviction.

The latest and possibly the last of the suspected Jack the Rippers is one of the most improbable. Yet Camps believed he was the true murderer. The suspect was the son of a Dorset doctor, a former public schoolboy, a briefless barrister who became a teacher and, if Daniel Farson is to be believed, a multiple murderer. His name was Montague John Drewitt and he ended his short life miserably in the Thames on the last day of December 1888.

The new theory is based on the information received by Farson following a television programme he arranged. The information came in the form of a letter from a Mr Knowles in Australia, who claimed to have seen a 'document' entitled 'The East End Murderer – I Knew Him'. The author was said to be Lionel Drewitt who, as it turned out, was a cousin of Montague Drewitt. Montague was suspected as the Ripper, but never named, by no less a person than Sir Melville Macnaghten.

The actual 'document' was borrowed or stolen from Farson's dossier on the case and Farson's extensive enquiries and travels in Australia failed to bring it to light. But Farson remembers from his notes that it established beyond doubt that Lionel Drewitt before emigrating to Australia practised as a doctor in the Minories, the street that connects Aldgate with the Tower of London, in the area where the murders were committed. As boys in Dorset, the cousins

Montague and Lionel lived a few miles apart and often saw each other. The supposition is that when both lived in London the friendship was resumed and Montague often visited Lionel at his surgery in the Minories.

From this base, or even from his own base in the Temple, it is thought that Montague made forays to commit the Ripper murders. Montague's mother was insane and there is a strong presumption that another cousin William, as well as Lionel, knew that Montague was also insane – 'sexually' insane, as Sir Melville Macnaghten describes it in private notes to which Farson has had access. The theory of insanity is supported by a pathetic suicide note found in Montague's chambers in which he said he felt he was going to be like his mother and the best thing for him was to go.

As with some of the other theories the facts fit, and Camps, with his knowledge of the workings of the criminal mind, came down in favour of the Farson theory.

Ten

Work at
Pentonville

From the start of his association with Sir Bentley Purchase, Camps'
professional work often took him to the grim Pentonville Prison
to carry out post mortems after executions. At the beginning of
1952 he was there for one on a West African named Backary
Mauneh, who had been stabbed in a fight in St Pancras, London,
with a ship's greaser, Joseph Aku. There had been an argument
about a packet of 'reefers' or Indian hemp cigarettes. The knives
had come out, people had screamed, police whistles had blown,
crowds gathered, and finally an ambulance had taken Aku to hospital,
where he died soon after arrival. Mauneh received a badly cut hand
but while waiting for the ambulance he had the presence of mind
to relieve his injured countryman of his gold watch.

Camps often had the experience of performing the post mortems
on both victims and their murderers but in this case he did not
carry out that on the victim. If he had done so, even with his
knowledge of violent death, Camps would have been surprised at
the devastating nature of the victim's injuries. Mauneh was a strong
man and before the knife fight had struck Aku so violently in the
face with his fist that he had loosened his teeth and spread his flat
features further still. While Aku was cowering away, Mauneh
stabbed him in the neck from behind with such ferocity that his
spinal cord had been cut through. The result must have been almost
instantaneous paralysis.

The trial itself at the Old Bailey was notable for at least two
features. Mauneh swore that every one of the forty witnesses called
for the prosecution was either mistaken or lying; and when Mr
Justice Gorman was about to sentence Mauneh to death, a man in
the well of the court enlivened the proceedings by shouting: 'In

the name of God, take that black cap off and abide by the word of God: "Thou shalt not kill." ' '

One result of the trial was Camps' presence at Pentonville on 27 May shortly before 8 a.m., where he found Sir Bentley Purchase, in whose North London district the prison stood, shuffling through the official papers dismissing Mauneh's appeal against conviction, legalizing the execution, ordering it to take place, and finally requiring an inquest to be held on the hanged man's body.

The law took its course, Mauneh died, and pathologist and coroner waited patiently for an hour after the execution before completing the business. Camps' post mortem took the same form as any other. But this was a charade. The dead man's neck had been broken by judicial hanging and everybody knew it. Camps and Purchase were representing the public and though there was always a possibility that something might go wrong at an execution – Bentley Purchase once told me that he had seen the necks of hanged men stretched by as much as a yard or more, which might easily lead to severed heads – it would still have done the dead man no good to have the matter broadcast. On such sombre occasions, Camps always made a complete post mortem.

In Mauneh's case, as usual, the coroner had before him the prison doctor's report that the execution had been carried out 'humanely and expeditiously'. There was no hitch and death was instantaneous. Camps made his independent report on the body to the coroner. He spoke of a well-nourished, healthy man whose neck had been broken. He had not eaten a hearty breakfast and there was no food in the stomach at all. He found no alcohol but there was a small quantity of water.

The coroner's officer, presumably for convenience's sake, had rounded up ten men from the same street near the prison to serve on the jury. They returned a formal verdict, received a fee of 2s, signed a receipt for it and left. By this time Camps was on his way to another post mortem.

Later that year, Camps was to carry out post mortems on other young men who had been sentenced to death for murder by means of stabbing. In the early fifties knives were easier to come by than guns, and in crimes in which women were involved men who had them did not seem reluctant to use them.

John Howard Godar, a film cameraman from Uxbridge, who at thirty-one should have learned more self-control, even though his mind might have been full of dramatic film situations, stabbed his twenty-year-old girl friend Maureen Cox time and time again with a stiletto. Another of Camps' cases concerned Raymond Jack Cull, from Northolt. He had been married only a few months but was living apart from his young wife. He sought her out at her parents' house and killed her with a more substantial weapon – a bayonet. Yet another murderer, Dennis George Muldourney, the resident Irish porter at the respectable Reform Club, killed his sweetheart with a sheath knife at a Kensington hotel. Peter Cyril Johnson, a coloured barrow-boy, the odd man out, did not use a knife to kill a friend in a fit of fury in a Bethnal Green street. He used something even more horrible : a big, jagged piece of concrete which he found in a nearby gutter.

Before the post mortem reports went into the archives, the final notes could be assembled concerning the last minutes in the lives of the condemned men. It was found that Godar had had some whisky with his breakfast, Cull had had neither whisky nor breakfast and Muldourney and Johnson had faced breakfast but had done without the last traditional glass of whisky. It is doubtful whether any of the many murderers on whom Camps performed post mortems ever drank their last drink as a toast.